KU-694-198

Assessing and Managing Risk

For Thomas and Bethan

ASSESSING AND MANAGING

Risk

by Steve Morgan

Practitioner's Handbook

The Sainsbury Centre
for Mental Health

Pavilion
PUBLISHING

ASSESSING AND MANAGING RISK

Practitioner's handbook

Steve Morgan

The Sainsbury Centre for Mental Health

First published 1998. Reprinted 1999 (three times).

Published by
Pavilion Publishing (Brighton) Limited
8 St George's Place
Brighton
East Sussex BN1 4GB

Telephone: 01273 623222

Fax: 01273 625526

Email: pavpub@pavilion.co.uk

Web: www.pavpub.com

© The Sainsbury Centre for Mental Health, 1998.

Pavilion Publishing is committed to providing high-quality, good-value training materials and conferences, and bringing new ideas to all those involved in health and social care. Founded by health and social care professionals, Pavilion has maintained its strong links with key agencies in the field, giving us a unique opportunity to help people develop the skills they need through our publications, conferences and training.

The author has asserted his rights in accordance with the *Copyright, Designs and Patents Act, 1988*, to be identified as the author of this title.

ISBN 1 900600 34 X

A catalogue record for this title is available from the British Library.

All rights reserved. No part of this publication may be reproduced, stored in a retrieval system, or transmitted in any form or by any means, electronic, mechanical, photocopying, recording or otherwise, without the prior permission of the publishers.

Editor: Jane Moody

Page design and typesetting: Stanford Douglas Associates

Cover design: Métier Design

Printing: Page Bros. (Norwich)

CONTENTS

Acknowledgements vi

Introduction 1
Aims of the Practitioner's handbook. 3
Structure of the Practitioner's handbook. 3

Chapter One CONCEPTS OF RISK 5
Introduction. 5
The meaning of risk 6
The language of risk 10
Categories of risk. 11
The process approach 13
Risk and expectations 14
Risk and dangerousness. 16
Risk-taking versus defensive practice 18

Chapter Two RISK ASSESSMENT. 21
Introduction. 21
Research evidence 22
Literature review 24
Risk assessment for whom?. 25
Potential impact on staff 26
What are we assessing? 27
Purpose of assessment. 28
Methods of assessment 29
Frequency of assessment 30
Clinical considerations 31
Recording the assessment 36

Chapter Three RISK MANAGEMENT 43
Introduction. 43
Literature review 44
Procedural context. 45
Procedural skills. 47

Clinical team procedures 49
Managing risk behaviours 49
Clinical strategies. 51
Personal skills 56
Recording risk management plans 61
Staff training issues 62

Chapter Four   SERVICE ORGANISATION. 65
Introduction. 65
Highlighting service failings 66
Organisational requirements 70

Chapter Five   ACCOUNTABILITY AND RESPONSIBILITY 75
Introduction. 75
Levels of responsibility 77
Inquiries and courts 80

Appendix 1   QUESTIONING SOMEONE ABOUT THEIR RISK POTENTIAL 83
Introduction. 83
Suicide and self-harm 84
Violence 85

Appendix 2   OUTLINE RISK ASSESSMENT FORMAT 87

Appendix 3   OUTLINE RISK MANAGEMENT PLAN 91

References   95

'If you don't risk anything, you may risk everything.'

Acknowledgements

Special thanks are extended to the following for their help and advice in the process of revising the content: Paul O'Halloran, Head of Practice Development and Training at the Sainsbury Centre for Mental Health; Peter Ryan, Director of Mental Health at Middlesex University; Phillip Vaughan, Project Manager, Forensic Project Team, The Wessex Consortium. I would also like to thank Salford Mental Health Services for providing the basis for a line of questioning in **Appendix 1**.

INTRODUCTION

Whether or not risk is at the top of the national agenda for mental health, managers and practitioners exercise assessments of risk and make risk decisions as an intrinsic part of their daily activity. The relative allocation of resources for different team functions, or the awareness of the level of tension being expressed by a service user during a home visit, are each examples of the many appreciations of elements of risk made on a routine basis.

Furthermore, when we shift our attention away from the realms of mental health, we may appreciate that risk is central to most aspects of human activity. We all exercise choices: who to meet? where to go? how to get there? what to do? One choice made eliminates others and binds us in relative terms to the consequences of that choice. We choose pathways in life we wish to follow, and we change directions according to internal and external influences. Our responses to risks help to shape us as individuals, with different degrees of autonomy and personal identity. In essence, risk can be seen to possess positive qualities that can greatly shape our own development.

We may think of sky-divers or racing drivers as slightly perverse in the choices they make, yet there are very few of us who do not openly or secretly hold their challenges and achievements in awe. We may even fantasise what it would be like for us to face the same challenges. Yet when a person is identified as having a mental illness, the media, government and society are unified in conferring on the managers and practitioners of mental health services a duty of care, which in practice becomes a predominantly restrictive function. A service user is generally viewed as someone for whom risk is a negative entity, with dire personal consequences as the inevitable outcome. The opportunity to develop through constructive risk-taking is often denied or suppressed by a preoccupation with the negative aspects of risk to self and others.

Undoubtedly, risk is high on the mental health agenda. A series of high profile public inquiries into incidents of homicide and serious self-harm, committed by people experiencing mental health problems, has provided the media with opportunities to fashion the public imagination. The result is widespread fear of mental illness and of the policy of community care which supposedly raises the incidence of harm. Public unease translates into a political issue requiring government sympathies and rapid responses. The tragedy of these incidents should not be down-played, but their frequency and potential seem to be artificially elevated, in a way that is not necessarily reflected in the published research (Bennett, 1996).

The bulk of attention is paid to the category of harm to others, despite the evidence that this is considerably smaller than the risks service users experience against themselves (Reed, 1997). While a link is established between mental illness and violence, its incidence is rare and should not be exaggerated to the stigmatising levels the media generates in public perceptions. However, neither should any other party play down the devastation of the impact of any incident on all those who are close to the victims.

The government response of the 1990s has been a plethora of guidance and legislation issued for local implementation, on a scale not previously seen. Managers and practitioners alike now fear the next news broadcast of yet another mental patient 'let loose' to commit a serious offence; the implication being that they are inadequately supervised. Managers fear the negative scrutiny and publicity of their service, while practitioners anticipate the spectre of being individually blamed and scapegoated for failing to do their job properly (or as they perceive it, failing to meet impossible expectations). The continuing level of inquiries, running at approximately 30 per year (Muijen, 1997a), reflects a level of tragedy that all service providers are working to minimise. Yet the calls for a retreat to greater levels of institutional care are often made without an appreciation of the equally significant tragedy that approximately one service user a week dies as a consequence of their contact with the mental health services that are attempting to treat and support them (Mind, 1994).

On the one hand, the challenge posed is that of improving our abilities to assess, predict and manage risks in a climate where the protection of society is raised as the necessary consequence of pursuing a liberal policy of community care. On the other hand, we have a duty to provide care and support in the least restrictive methods and environments, through respecting the individuality of people (their behaviours, their wishes and their needs).

The voices of society, the media, the government and the service-user movement have all grown louder and more vociferous on issues of mental health service provision. All claim to know what is needed, but their interests are frequently poles apart. Yet managers and practitioners in mental health services, both in the statutory and voluntary sectors, are required to negotiate conflicting demands and demonstrate that they have responded to all the changing demands on their services.

Whatever philosophical standpoint is adopted, serious and fatal incidents continue to occur and will continue to do so, with or without well-resourced mental health services. Practitioners may perceive scapegoating as part of the need to allocate blame in response to a tragedy and may feel this to be an unfair reflection on them. However, there are real and reasonable expectations that individuals will be accountable and responsible for demonstrating standards of professional competence and good practice. Accountability and responsibility can be identified at individual, team and organisational levels. Clarity of these points will help to reduce the perception of individual scapegoating.

A further challenge is one of placing the whole issue of risk in mental health into its real context. This should lead to a better appreciation of more realistic expectations than can be made on individuals and services that work with the less predictable areas of human behaviour. Practitioners do have to face the very real challenge of engaging people who are mistrustful of services and who have a history of high risk to themselves or others. Difficult decisions often have to be faced about how to manage unpredictable and risky behaviours. However, it is unrealistic to set the burden of expectation at the level of risk elimination. Risk minimisation, and the continuing review of what constitutes best practice in areas of risk, should be more widely appreciated by the different stakeholders who express views on the mental health services.

Aims of the Practitioner's handbook

It is the intention to promote good practice in the training of staff and the overall understanding *by* staff of the concepts and issues influencing risk. Practitioners should feel equipped to carry out clinical risk assessment effectively. The linking of this information to multidisciplinary risk management, and the understanding of realistic expectations around accountability and responsibility which accompanies this handbook is designed to offer workshop opportunities to share ideas and develop locally relevant agreements on policy and procedures in response to the challenges of risk.

The **Practitioner's handbook** aims to:

- summarise current literature and research findings for busy practitioners who do not have the time to review this information themselves

- offer guidelines to good practice in assessing and managing a range of risks encountered in clinical situations

- pose questions to help the reader adapt the knowledge to the circumstances of their own local service context

- provide supplementary materials for people attending and/or using the **Trainer's manual** in workshop settings.

This handbook is not an exhaustive account of the complex issues and concepts of risk: ideas, views and research evidence are extensive and diverse. However, it should present a guide to thinking through many issues in the context of local circumstances.

Structure of the Practitioner's handbook

Risk has become an emotive subject in relation to mental health services, on which everyone has a viewpoint but few are expected to act decisively. It may not be sufficient to offer individual service providers a risk assessment tool, and guidance on the care programme approach as the method of effective risk management. We should, at least, expect the managers and practitioners of services concerned with serious mental illness to have a basic understanding of the complex issues and concepts of the broader discussion of risk.

For this purpose, the handbook is divided into the following sections, to reflect the main areas of concern expressed by practitioners in training workshops on issues of risk:

Chapter One: Concepts of risk

Chapter Two: Risk assessment

Chapter Three: Risk management

Chapter Four: Service organisation

Chapter Five: Accountability and responsibility

'Service user individuality' and 'local service context' cannot be emphasised too strongly. Generalisations offered in this text should be carefully scrutinised and interpreted within these parameters.

CHAPTER ONE

CONCEPTS OF RISK

Introduction

As a concept, risk is widely established in our daily language and activity, but its manifestations in practice vary greatly. Consider:

- the business and financial sectors
- betting on the horses
- unprotected sex
- hospital admission and discharge
- tightrope walking
- marriage.

The indication of risk is interpreted and defined very differently in each of the above activities.

In your consideration of working with people experiencing serious mental illness, it is important to understand what you mean by the risks that have to be identified and managed. The professional and personal attitudes formed from training and experience, combined with an understanding of risk, will help to shape your approach to working with different levels and frequencies of risk.

Your conceptualisation of risk should examine how you categorise the different risks you may encounter. Do you view risk as:

- an **entity**, in terms of a tangible event and outcome; for example, a threat of violence resulting in injury?
- a **process** made up of interrelated functions; for example, a behavioural response to life events, brought about by particular social interactions, which could be identified and avoided?
- a **predictable**, and thus preventable, characteristic of human behaviour?
- an **unpredictable**, and thus impulsive, characteristic of human behaviour?

The practical manifestation of risk in mental health is appearing to become increasingly embedded in a conflict:

- on the one hand, there is the need for cautious defensive practice, based on an assumption that restriction will prevent some incidents

- on the other hand, there is a desire to promote positive risk-taking, based on the assumption that freedom of choice within an environment of support may reduce the need for some incidents.

For the practitioner, the reality is attempting to find a middle ground between these extremes.

The meaning of risk

Negative interpretations

Negative interpretations are the outcomes witnessed most frequently through media sensationalism of mental health and community care. In this context, dictionary definitions partially allude to risk as:

- danger
- loss
- damage
- injury.

It is frequently linked to fears of disastrous or detrimental outcomes.

CASE EXAMPLE

Malcolm is a 46-year-old man, with a 23-year history of manic depression, including several hospital admissions commonly under compulsory detention. Frequent threatening behaviours have been accompanied by an apparent lack of insight, and perpetual blaming of others has resulted in loss of family contact, partners, home and ultimately his liberty, as a result of escalating threats.

Most plans developed with Malcolm result in conflict. Health and local authorities stress the need for highly supported accommodation, leading on to more independent living. Malcolm rejects any such delay in returning to his own accommodation, with no medical or community support necessary. A stalemate ensues, with Malcolm threatening harm to others, or suicide as his only other option.

■ **What is your immediate emotional response to the predicament faced by Malcolm and the service providers, in these circumstances?**

Positive interpretations

Some dictionary definitions of the term 'risk' highlight potentially positive experiences:

- accepting a challenge in order to progress forward
- to gain a desired outcome
- weighing up the pros and cons is occasionally seen as a positive feature of taking a gamble
- opportunity and new experience.

CASE EXAMPLE

Tunde is a 33-year-old man with a history of two episodes of a severe manic depressive illness, requiring compulsory hospital admissions. He has a good academic record, including a period of employment in a teaching capacity. He wishes to further his education, successfully achieving an unconditional placement at his first choice of university. Tunde's primary concern is that the oral medication may slow his thinking and impede his academic pursuits. He negotiates a ceasing of medication, on the basis that his case manager will maintain regular contact. The focus of the relationship is to monitor stress-coping mechanisms and observe for early warning signs of relapse. He now states that the two episodes of illness were clearly linked to cannabis use, from which he has long since abstained. He also admits that he has not taken the medication for several months and points to evidence of remaining well. The plan of support is agreed, with no medication currently prescribed.

- **What is your immediate understanding of the challenges faced by Tunde and the service providers, in these circumstances?**

Practitioner response

Your response to different interpretations of risk will be partly determined by:

- individual practitioner values and attitudes towards service users defined by risk behaviours
- principles underlying your team and service priorities
- roles defined by professional background and training.

- **What conditions may need to be in place to ensure practitioners remain open to the possibility of different interpretations of risk, in different service user circumstances?**

Definitions of risk

In its simplest form, risk is seen as 'the probability of an event happening' (ILPS, 1995). An event broadens the concept beyond the more usual references to the likelihood of violence (Snowden, 1997). It would also embrace categories of suicide and self-harm, and of severe self-neglect (NHS Executive, 1994). Some definitions have sought to emphasise a balance by introducing the potential for beneficial, as well as harmful, outcomes (Carson, 1995).

A further addition of 'stated timescale' extends to a definition of 'the potential predictive value of likely outcomes' (Alberg *et al.*, 1996).

Naughton (1996), in a newspaper column not focusing specifically on mental health, casts some doubts over definitions, suggesting that: *'there is no such thing as risk. There are only perceptions of risk'.* He reminds us of the importance of context when considering the concept. The same event seen in different circumstances gives rise to a different perception of the risk. Thus, risk becomes a social construction rather than an objective reality.

Bowers (1997) suggests that the concept *'is not a discrete phenomenon. It is continuous, fluid, messy, unpredictable, and exists within and across a number of different dimensions — usually simultaneously'.* Her attempt to broaden the concept introduces the notion that we are often faced with dilemmas rather than straight choices. There is no clear right or wrong answer, but we do have to make risk decisions that are *'well informed, based on clear rationale and owned by the individuals, the team and the organisation'.*

Risk in mental health is a far less clear concept than it is in other branches of health care, or even in many fields of industry or science. Predicting events and outcomes in the realm of human behaviour is inexact. To leave such an unpredictable, yet emotive, subject to individual clinicians alone overlooks the collective accountability that should be distributed at the three levels of individual, team and organisation, referred to by Bowers above. Government, media and society also share a responsibility to reach realistic expectations of what can be achieved within this area of practice.

My own favoured approach to a definition would be:

'Risk is the likelihood of an identified behaviour occurring in response to changing personal circumstances. The outcomes are more frequently harmful for self or others, though occasionally they may have a beneficial aim in pursuit of a positive change.'

■ **What practical value and guidance may a definition of risk offer to your team and your organisation?**

Defining the client group

Definitions of severe mental illness have most frequently debated the relative importance of three main factors (Bachrach, 1988):

- diagnosis
- duration
- disability.

The more recent prominence of risk on the mental health agenda has been mirrored by the addition of:

- safety
- informal/formal support

(Department of Health, 1995).

The significance of definitions can be more closely linked to the targets and priorities agreed at the local service level. Clear client group definitions can be an aid to the allocation of resources, through the configuration of local service structures. At a general level, client groups identified for targeting in relation to their presentations of risk, have included:

- predominantly psychotic diagnosis with negative features of neglect, social isolation, poverty of thought and speech; frequently aged over 40 years

- predominantly psychotic diagnosis; younger, more volatile and unstable in presentation, with active florid symptoms, and aggressive behaviours

- dual diagnosis; predominantly psychosis with significant drug or alcohol abuse.

> ■   **What impact do local definitions of client groups have on the allocation of resources in your services?**

What about personality disorder?

Personality disorder is a more contentious issue for definition of target client groups. The NHS Executive (1994) *Introduction of Supervision Registers* states that the diagnosis of a personality disorder, including psychopathic disorders, is to be included within the context of mental illness *'if they are receiving treatment from specialist psychiatric services'*.

One question is whether a personality disorder is treatable in a medical sense, or whether it is a matter of personal responsibility for actions and behaviours, to be processed through the criminal justice system.

'Personality disorders are considered to be present when an abnormality of personality causes severe problems either to the individual or to others. They are thought to be caused by adverse early experience and are often preceded by conduct disorders in childhood.' (Alberg et al., 1996)

Anti-social personality disorders, specifically psychopathic disorders, are thought to be closely linked to violent behaviour patterns.

The non-medical interventions developed through psychosocial approaches to behaviour disturbance are arguably more relevant to the treatment and response to these conditions.

However, the links and responsibilities between the mental health and criminal justice systems need to be clarified (Home Office and Department of Health, 1992).

If the mental health system refuses to accept responsibility for a person labelled with a personality disorder, greater clarity is required about the label and why it is not treatable. Furthermore, we need to acknowledge that the criminal justice system may more frequently interpret the term to mean mental illness.

The outcome can be one of confusion, with neither system adopting lead responsibility, leaving a potentially dangerous individual unsupervised and unsupported. It is precisely the people who fall into this category who are more frequently involved in serious incidents and who cause the general public most fear and concern.

> ■ **What is your local understanding of agreements within services, and between sectors, regarding responsibility for people with the label of 'personality disorder'?**

The language of risk

The broader conceptualisation of risk involves many facets, which collectively form a *process approach*.

Risk policy

A risk policy is a clearly documented and communicated set of statements, agreed by professional bodies, employers, and team managers. The purpose of these statements is to guide, encourage and support the informed risk decisions and practice of individual service practitioners in their interactions with service users.

Risk assessment

Risk assessment is an examination of the context and the detail of past risk incidents, in the light of current circumstances. From this we extrapolate predictions of the future likelihood of risk behaviours. Assessment may be individualised to the history of one person. Prediction may also involve judgements on the probability of outcomes against the beneficial or harmful value of those outcomes, based on group data. The outcome of an assessment should be a formulation, on which to base decisions and plans.

Risk factors

Risk factors are specific circumstances that may affect the intensity or likelihood of risk behaviours translating into real outcomes.

Risk decision making

Risk decision making is the link between risk assessment and risk management. It uses the element of prediction as a basis for identifying the balance between the benefits and harms of risk behaviours. Risk decisions will form the basis for the subsequent planning process.

Risk management

Risk management is a statement of plans and allocation of responsibilities, to support, contain or respond to the risk decisions and/or enactment of risk behaviours. The risk management plan will outline the assessment formulation into actions for clinical practice. The clinical risk management plan will identify all members of the team, including the service user and carers.

Risk procedures

Risk procedures are the agreement of the team and service mechanisms for reviewing and implementing clinical risk management plans. They include the local agreement on implementation of the relevant guidance and legislation outlined in the risk policy.

■ **What elements of a risk policy are in place, and what needs to be addressed further, in your local service?**

Categories of risk

From an understanding of meaning, we can begin to categorise the sources and types of risk most commonly addressed in mental health services.

Sources of risk (by focus):

- individual risk — individual behaviour
- situational risk — context and environment
- system risk — organisation and communication

(Carson, 1995).

Types of risk (by behaviour):

- aggression and violence
- suicide and self-harm
- severe self-neglect

(NHS Executive, 1994).

Definitions of risk behaviours

Aggression

'A hostile or offensive action or mental attitude, delivered within the controls of acceptable behavioural limits, in response to a perceived or real provocation.'

Aggression has a place in everyday living. It acts either as a safety valve for keeping others at a distance, or for forcing overdue decisions or actions to be taken. When the normal controls on aggressive behaviours are exceeded, then violence occurs.

Violence

'An expression of anger, fear or despair, through an extreme and forceful delivery of actions and emotions, inflicting harmful or damaging effects.'

Violence would include actual physical assault on another individual, extreme outpouring of verbal or written threats, and damage to property.

Suicide and self-harm

'The inflicting of damage or injury to self, with an intention of relieving extreme tension or distress, or drawing attention to a need for help, or causing death.'

This category of risk includes suicidal behaviours with a planned intent, suicidal behaviours as a call for help, attention through cutting or mutilation, and abusing or addictive behaviours with the intention of inflicting harm or injury.

Severe self-neglect

'The act of disregarding care for self, with the consequence of serious risk to personal health and well-being.'

Neglect of treatment and daily care may lead to a deterioration of physical health and condition, mental and environmental health. Degrees of self-neglect may also endanger other carers or people who come into contact with the individual. To be described as severe self-neglect will require multiple factors, rather than one isolated area of neglect.

These definitions are meant to act as a guide to your understanding of the more frequently experienced categories of behavioural risk. Caution needs to be exercised when reviewing the research and literature, as different writers may employ slightly different definitions of a behaviour; for example, for some, violence may include actual physical harm, or physical and emotional harm, but not damage to property.

While the above categories are the most frequently described in the literature, they are by no means the only categories of risk encountered. Consider the following examples of other categories:

- exploitation
- sexual abuse
- substance abuse
- other?

■ **What categories of risk can you identify on your current individual and/or team caseload?**

Sources of risk

The above categories identify *individual* risk behaviours. However, attention should not be focused entirely on risk as an innate personality trait, thus labelling people as 'risky individuals'. People fitting this description are extremely rare.

Most people behaving in a risky manner do so in response to situations, circumstances, or personal relationships. It is perhaps more useful to view incidents of risk in their context of cumulative events and environmental influences (Prins, 1986).

Risk assessment will, in part, identify the behaviour, but should also concern itself with identifying the triggers through events leading up to, and producing, the risk behaviour.

The systems governing our working practices also contribute to the potential for the very risks they attempt to avoid. The fact that services are organised into different sectors and authorities sets up difficulties for effective communication. Professional and non-professional boundaries, underpinned by personalities, hierarchies and pressured workloads, all conspire to enable the potential for risks to occur.

A reliance on emphasising accountability within the procedural arrangements before positive encouragement and support generates feelings of fear rather than confidence in skills. However, accountability for actions is a real issue that all practitioners must face and will be discussed further in **Chapter Five**.

> ■ **How may the inter-agency procedures in your local services contribute to the potential for risks to occur?**

The process approach

The individual incident of risk is an entity that can be described as a behaviour attributable to a person, a place, and a time. However, concepts of prevention, containment, and minimisation require that we do more than simply describe events after they have occurred.

The broader concept of risk can be articulated as a process which incorporates the links between the many elements outlined previously in the section **The language of risk**.

In its simplest form, we may view this as a cyclical process, as in **Figure One**, overleaf, whereby **risk assessment** aims to identify individual and group data **risk factors**; these in turn will inform the **risk decisions**, which will be implemented through **risk procedures** into an overall **risk management** plan. Review of the plans will inform the ongoing risk assessment.

Encompassing the whole cycle would be the organisation and inter-agency statements of risk policy.

Monahan (1993) uses the term *risk containment* to describe a process including a broad range of clinical issues: risk assessment, risk management, service policies and guidelines that set out the need for an information database supported by good quality documentation and a damage control system.

Snowden (1997) suggests that *'The assessment and management of risk is an approach rather than a skill'*. It requires clinical practice exposure above the more traditional methods of teaching. While specific clinical skills are essential to effective assessment and management, the broader process consideration of risk should be adopted as an approach to the planning and implementation of interventions in a context of working with high risk.

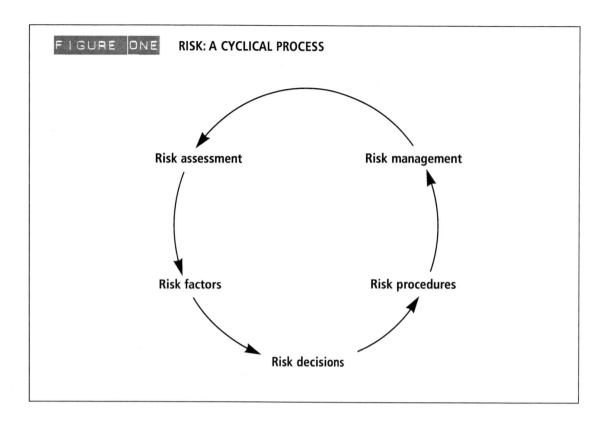

FIGURE ONE   **RISK: A CYCLICAL PROCESS**

Risk assessment

Risk management

Risk factors

Risk procedures

Risk decisions

Risk and expectations

A perceived fear held by many practitioners is that the media-driven public and government expectation of clinical services is one of risk elimination. Despite the ever-growing body of guidance and legislation on the subject, incidents resulting in public inquiries are running at a constant level. The ill-informed reaction frequently reported is that the policy of community care has failed, yet mental health and risk are both highly unpredictable.

Recent attitudes in the psychiatric press take a very different perspective from the national media on issues of risk. Health sources (Tyrer & Kennedy, 1995) and legal sources (Carson, 1995) share similar opinions, that however competent the clinicians, and however thorough the management procedures and plans may be, incidents will still occur because of the unpredictability involved in this area.

The elimination of 100% of risk is simply unrealistic and an unhelpful expectation that only serves to instil negative practices and the fear of individual scapegoating. Realistically, we can expect the pursuit of risk minimisation through learning and applying knowledge of good practice. Particular attention needs to be paid to accessing all relevant information, reasoned decisions based on the information that is available, and co-ordinating the input of different people through coherent plans and actions.

> ■ **Where do the real and perceived expectations of your individual and team practice originate?**

Prediction

Access information, determine the risk factors, identify the early warning signs and develop a clear and comprehensive plan of intervention. Prediction could not be simpler and prevention must surely be the outcome. This assumption relies on good quality assessment tools; but probably also on people remaining consistent in their behaviour patterns. Both of these assumptions are somewhat dangerous to rely on. We know that people are not consistent in their behaviour, even without the experience of mental health problems. It is also safe to say that our current assessment of situations and of the precipitants of incident is better in hindsight.

Moore (1996) suggests, in relation to violence, *'The many and diverse pieces of research about prediction of risk differ widely on almost every point except one; that we are not always very good at it'*. Opinions differ from 60–70% accuracy at the optimistic end, to 5% accuracy at the pessimistic end.

Hawton (1994) offers a number of reasons why prediction is poor in relation to suicide, which may translate equally to other categories:

- incidence is rare and predictors are crude
- research focuses on completed events and may not necessarily generalise as accurate prediction
- short-term risk and long-term risk are different
- most risk factors, with the exception of gender, fluctuate in magnitude
- most studies focus on generalised group characteristics, which are not necessarily helpful for prediction with individuals.

Reed (1997) echoes this last point when he suggests that we have a good understanding of the general picture of risk factors, but bridging the gap from the general to the particular presents greater difficulty.

Some of the ethical issues of our classification of prediction are discussed by Moore (1996) and Duggan (1997a). How many *false positives* (risk predicted, but not presented) and *false negatives* (risk presented, but not predicted) are society and mental health services prepared to carry?

Bingley (1997) reminds us, that in the case of false positives, we are judging people incorrectly in the complete absence of any offence.

Bacon (1997) also discusses the implications of risk assessment practice on individual liberties. He suggests that the response of the professionals to their poor predictive abilities is to become overcautious, through more defensive and restrictive practices.

Wessely (1997) discusses the research into links between violence and mental illness. He particularly highlights the divergent opinions regarding the prevalence of the link drawn by leading criminologists on the one hand and forensic psychiatrists on the other. Such divergence does little to promote confidence in the practitioner's abilities to predict risk.

Duggan (1997a) points out that the evidence of the respective predictive merits of forensic psychiatrists, general psychiatrists, other mental health professionals and non-professionals is also conflicting in its conclusions.

Buchanan (1997) offers some scope for confidence, pointing to evidence of clinical directions where predictive abilities do appear to be improving. The influence of specific delusional beliefs on individual behaviour is now a better understood marker of potential risks.

■ **What pressures do you perceive within your own practice, and/or service, to be influencing a need to predict more accurately the potential for risk incidents?**

Risk and dangerousness

Issues that were traditionally seen as the concern of a small group, namely forensic psychiatrists special-ising in the assessment and treatment of mentally disordered offenders, have now become a central concern of all mental health professionals (Rose, 1998). This shifting emphasis may be closely linked with changing priorities, from a concept of **dangerousness** to one of **risk** (Maden, 1996; Duggan, 1997a), see *Table One*, opposite.

Snowden (1997) reminds us that forensic psychiatrists have been seen as the experts in the field of dangerousness, largely by other clinicians, perhaps attributing to them some perceived special skills that they themselves do not possess. However, forensic psychiatrists do no more than apply the basic skills of general psychiatry, but to a specifically defined population. One forensic psychiatrist even suggested that *'It is patience, thoroughness and persistence in this process rather than any diagnostic brilliance that produces results. In this sense, the telephone, the written request for past records, and the checking of information against other informants, are the important diagnostic devices'* (Scott, 1977).

Reed (1997) indicates that the literature on the relationship of mental disorder and dangerous behaviour is vast, but that recent developments have helped us towards a clearer idea of the circumstances in which the mentally disordered may behave in a dangerous manner, rather than simply seeing individuals as dangerous people. Rose outlines a chronological view of the shift from seeing dangerousness as a characteristic of certain types of people in the 1960s; mutating into a matter of 'factors, situations and statistical probabilities' in the 1970s and 1980s. The prominence of 'risk' as a concept is more clearly identified by the 1990s, through a substantial increase in the real number, and relative proportion, of published articles in relation to those on dangerousness.

Rose suggests that, more recently, all patients can be crudely allocated to a level of risk: risk assessed, risk classified, risk managed; high risk, medium risk, low risk — but rarely no risk. Risk management is no longer a matter of hospital admission or prison sentence and is not to be seen as solely concerned with the mentally disordered offender — but is now to be seen as relating to the everyday life of all service users and service providers. In the criminal justice system, dangerousness may be seen to focus on the actuarial methods of prediction as the basis of clinical judgement, requiring practitioners to make bold statements of potential behaviour. However, in the mental health system, the progressive move to community-based services has raised the prominence of estimating fluctuating levels of risk, in relation to a complexity of personal circumstances. This latter shift has also been accompanied by conflicting tensions between the concepts of care and control, and how they may be offered through service provision.

Snowden (1997) suggests *'It is debatable whether the notion of dangerousness now has any utilitarian value for psychiatry…dangerousness is nothing more than an adjective which has been elevated into a pseudo-scientific construct whose definitions amount to little more than "past harm predicts future behaviour"'*.

TABLE ONE RISK AND DANGEROUSNESS — DISTINGUISHING CHARACTERISTICS

Risk	**Dangerousness**
• open to objective assessment	• more subjective
• open to enquiry	• more 'black and white'
• involves continuous assessment and review	• a major decision reviewed less frequently
• offers opportunities for empowering collaborative assessment	• a more stigmatising label
• encompasses a broad range of behaviours	• more clearly linked to aggression and violence
• involves administrative decision making	• more concerned with legal categorisation
• located on a continuum	• a binary distinction

(Based on Monahan & Steadman, 1994)

Risk and criminality

The link between mental disorder and criminal behaviour has been perpetuated through media attention on incidents of violence, specifically homicide. The presence of the speciality of forensic psychiatry helps to reinforce the link. Wessely (1997) has reviewed the epidemiology of crime, violence and schizophrenia. He concludes that there is no consistent evidence to support the assumption that the true prevalence of criminal behaviour among mental health service users exceeds true prevalence of criminal behaviour for the general population, when matched for demographic factors and prior criminality.

Furthermore, the literature highlights a contradiction: criminologists have researched large samples and concluded that mental illness is not a significant factor in the causes of crime. Psychiatrists have undertaken more detailed research of smaller samples, concluding that there is a higher rate of criminality in the mental health population than the general population. Wessely concludes that the crime rate in schizophrenia has increased over the last 30 years, but only in line with that of the general population. Consequently, community care does not appear to live up to its media-driven reputation for causing this type of increase.

So how significant is mental illness in the causes of criminal behaviour? Wessely reports that an estimate of *attributable risk* suggests that in the US, if schizophrenia could be eliminated, the crime rate would only drop by about 3%. We need to take account of the other significant factors, particularly substance abuse and previous offending.

> ■ **What relationships exist, in your local service, between the general and the forensic psychiatric services?**

Risk-taking versus defensive practice

The concept of risk, in the practice of individual clinicians, is embedded in a philosophical conflict. Recognising the needs of the service user does not always sit easily with the current emphasis on protecting the public from their real and perceived fears. Procedural arrangements frequently impact on individual liberties, but catastrophes require that something should be done (Duggan, 1997a). While many practitioners recognise the benefit of supporting service users to learn by taking chances and risks, they feel the overwhelming pressure to avoid errors. The prevailing climate in contemporary society is one of attributing blame when things go wrong. This is not simply a facet of mental health, as any cursory glance at the press will indicate. The fear of criticism and blame leads to an all too frequent, but understandable, retreat into defensive practice.

Harrison (1997) suggests we should be more explicit about the risks involved in defensive practice, particularly the failure to effectively involve and empower service users. He also suggests that the defensive walls of the physical institution will be replaced by defensive walls of care-programme approach paperwork.

Positive risk-taking

Should positive risk-taking be seen as a basic service user right, particularly as choice is something enjoyed by most of us? Risk-taking should be seen as a healthy part of community care, rather than as negligence or gambling with high stakes. It is the weighing up of different choices, gauging consequences, engaging the opportunities for support that emphasise learning rather than failure. Harrison suggests that risk-taking is an essential part of community care, which should be the mechanism that resists an ongoing tightening of procedures in the false expectation of the elimination of risk. The favoured approach should involve focusing on the more realistic goal of risk-minimisation.

Central to any positive risk-taking approach should be a genuine eliciting of the service user's real and perceived experiences of risk. The media and public image of the service user is that of perpetrator of risks to self and others. Whereas, a glance at the history of almost all service users indicates they are far more likely to be victims of risk, from a wide range of sources, most alarmingly from what are more frequently considered to be sources of care and support.

The following represents a range (not exhaustive) of sources of risk to users of mental health services:

- childhood sexual and physical abuse
- adult domestic violence
- threats and attacks from the local community
- an unsympathetic and fearful public
- social isolation

- loss of social and economic status through the stigma associated with mental health problems

- threatened or real loss of home

- distressing contacts with the criminal justice system

- relapse of illness and hospital admissions

- loss or deprivation of basic freedoms and human rights

- suicide attempts

- deaths through neuroleptic medication

- in-patient abuse and assaults, from patients and staff

- exploitation by misguided or criminal community workers.

We talk of integrating people into the community, but we often overlook just how threatening that community can be for a vulnerable person carrying the multiple burden of illness and stigma. Each of the above categories is an extremely rare event, but cumulatively they begin to give an impression of what a service user may have to face, either in reality or in their perceptions. When managing risk, these should be dismissed at your peril. Acknowledgement of these issues goes a long way to establishing the kind of engagement that may support more effective and collaborative risk management.

Elements of an empowering process

An empowering process works with a service user, placing them and their experience at the centre of the process. The following are some of the considerations you may put into practice:

- information is power, so share it

- empathic understanding of how and why an individual responds to their own experience of risk

- collaborative discussions of the links between past, present and future

- joint identification of early warning signs

- negotiation, with the service user holding the deciding vote

- open and creative use of the procedural arrangements, such as CPA, informing the service user of their central importance in all plans

- access to flexible and responsive support, and choices

- practising risk as a mutual learning process.

Defensive practice

Bingley (1997) refers to the moral and ethical challenges presented to service providers by the high costs of tragic outcomes. Where a culture of blame prevails, practitioners will inevitably feel pressure to guard against the potential for scapegoating and blame. Defensive practice is the most likely method of aiming to cover essential responsibilities, attempting to offset legal repercussions, or at least offering a damage limitation approach to minimising individual and organisational criticism.

Harris (1997) reminds us that difficult decisions have to be faced on a daily basis: balancing the risk of discharging a hospital in-patient against the risk of not admitting someone else who is relapsing in the community. Hospital bed management has become a constant challenge of weighing up the risks, particularly in the recent climate of bed closures and increased volume of involuntary admissions (Warren & Beadsmoore, 1997).

However, painting a negative picture of defensive practice is too simple. The reality is one of service providers having to make difficult decisions about a small minority of people who present very real dangers to themselves and others. The public have a right to expect that services will do all within their power and ability to ensure such risks are identified and properly managed. If such management is seen by some as a negative type of defensiveness, this should not detract from the need to restrict and detain in these rare circumstances.

It remains the best interest for some people to be detained when such high risks are identified, rather than suffer the inevitable consequences of a preventable tragedy. The aftermath for some will result in longer detention, increased stigma, and perpetual caution and restrictive responses. However, the danger is equally of concern that defensive practice results in over-caution, with a tendency to restrict on the basis of minimal risk potential. Infringements of civil liberties cannot be allowed to go ignored, or simply subjugated by a priority for public protection at all costs (Bacon, 1997).

> ■ **What examples can you identify of positive risk-taking and of defensive practice in your own clinical and/or managerial experiences?**

CHAPTER

 RISK ASSESSMENT

Introduction

Mental health service practitioners are required to undertake a comprehensive range of assessments as a routine responsibility of their work. Assessment is a particularly skilled and complex activity if it is to be performed effectively. It includes all, but not only, the following areas of interest:

- service user and carer involvement

- family and social systems assessment

- mental state examination

- adherence to medication and other treatment approaches

- risk assessment

- functional and task analyses

- personal strengths assessment.

Risk assessment needs to be seen within this wider context of service responsibilities. While it is something that we all do all the time — usually as a sub-conscious aspect of personal interactions and the exercising of decisions related to personal choices — it is nonetheless only one aspect of a comprehensive range of assessments.

Risk assessment is a process of identifying and investigating factors associated with an increased probability of specified risk behaviours occurring. It is also concerned with the patterns of circumstances in which these factors may arise. There are many types of risk that may be identified, for example, exploitation by others, sexual abuse, HIV and Aids, age-related vulnerability; but we are concerned here with the major categories identified in the introduction of supervision registers (NHS Executive, 1994):

- aggression and violence

- suicide and self-harm

- severe self-neglect.

By implication, we are focusing attention on the client group identified as people experiencing severe and enduring mental health problems. These will not only be people identified by supervision registers, though these will form the largest focus of our attention. Many people requiring accurate risk assessments will be identified more broadly by the local implementation of the CPA (these administrative procedures will be discussed more thoroughly in **Chapter Three: Risk management**).

We are not focusing on the issues associated with a risk of relapse of illness in the more general sense. This area of concern is one that belongs to the broader issue of assessment, of which risk assessment will contribute its part. Assessing and monitoring early warning signs will form a special area of interest in its own right, and will also contribute to effective risk assessment. By way of this illustration we begin to appreciate both the separateness and the interrelationship of the component parts of a comprehensive assessment.

Comprehensive assessment, across the range of activity, is a continuous process. The example of risk assessment is not a one-off exercise to fulfil hospital discharge procedures. As with other forms of assessment, it is an ongoing function of personnel across recognised service boundaries (preferably including the service user):

- hospital and community

- health and social care

- statutory and voluntary sectors

- primary care and secondary (specialist services) care

- formal and informal carers.

Placing risk assessment within the broader range of assessments should help us to maintain its focus on *care* rather than *control*. This will be further enhanced in **Chapter Three: Risk management**, by focusing attention on risk within the context of comprehensive treatment, support and rehabilitation. The issues of risk should not be seen to assume an over-arching influence on the whole picture of mental health service delivery, though clearly it is an integral part of it.

Before examining the details of performing risk assessments, a brief overview of the research evidence, and of some of the views in the literature will be presented. Together these form a rationale for the development of this guidance on assessment; but they may also offer directions for further investigation and information for the reader.

Research evidence

Some common themes emerge from research and from the literature:

- incidents of risk are rare

- mental illness is a significant factor when assessing the potential risk

- prediction is an uncertain activity.

Two major transatlantic studies are of significance to our understanding of assessing risks in mental health:

- Steadman *et al.* (1994) outline the MacArthur Risk Assessment Study, which is a US multi-site longitudinal study of approximately 1000 people. Its value lies in the elaboration of how a comprehensive risk assessment may be put into operation.

- Appleby (1997) provides an annual report of the UK *National Confidential Inquiry into Suicide and Homicide Involving People with Mental Illness*. By investigating national data it goes some way to indicating the size of the problems and the directions for further rigorous investigation.

Aggression and violence

Appleby (1997) states that 17% of people convicted of homicide (in the year up to May 1997) had symptoms of mental illness at the time of the offence; 5% had symptoms of psychosis. Also, in relation to a frequent fear in the general public, those with mental illness were less likely to have killed a stranger.

The Ritchie report (Ritchie *et al.*, 1994) is probably a defining document in respect of highlighting the individual and collective failings of the system through a detailed study of the care and treatment of one individual. Amongst its many findings, inadequate training in assessment procedures for identifying the substantial risks posed over a period of years was a clear deficiency.

McDonnell *et al.* (1994) point to evidence that suggests violent acts are not spontaneous. They usually arise out of an interaction of observable factors, at least in hindsight, but rarely 'out-of-the-blue'. A number of studies have indicated that clinicians' predictions are far from accurate. Whittington & Wykes (1994) report on studies where the service practitioners have had good knowledge of their service users, yet still perform poorly when required to predict incidents of risk behaviour.

Borum (1996) reports recent large scale studies that suggest mental disorder may be a robust and significant factor for the occurrence of violence. This has frequently been a point of debate in the literature.

Buchanan (1997) outlines research into the link of active delusions and subsequent acts of violence. Though there is a recognisable correlation, he argues the need for caution in interpreting the results. Further factors will be highlighted in the following literature review.

Suicide and self-harm

The size of the suicide problem is outlined by reports from the *National Confidential Inquiry into Suicide and Homicide by People with Mental Illness* (Amos, 1998):

* there are approximately 5000 suicides annually in the UK
* approximately 50% of these had contact with mental health services
* mental illness increases the risk ten-fold
* evidence suggests a failure to identify risk
* there is evidence of inadequate risk assessment.

McGovern (1996) reminds us that *'In a majority of cases, people who have committed suicide have been seen by a clinician no more than a month earlier and, in a substantial number, clinical improvements had been observed despite unresolved social or interpersonal problems'.*

Appleby (1997) states that the majority of suicides by people with a mental illness occur in situations in which risk is perceived to be low. Some 40% of post-hospital discharge suicides (during the year up to May 1997) occurred before the first follow-up appointments. This is more likely a reflection of the current knowledge on suicide risk, rather than a judgement on the quality of risk assessments.

The evidence highlights links to specific diagnosis, with the strongest indication being the prevalence of severe depression (Barraclough & Hughes, 1987). Psychotic diagnoses also rated high — schizophrenia (10%) and manic depression (15%) — in the analysis of suicide statistics (Appleby, 1992; Hawton, 1994).

The suicide rate in men is twice that among women and in both sexes the rate rises with age (Kreitman, 1988). In recent years, much attention has been drawn to the significant increase in suicide rates of young men (Burton *et al.*, 1990). The most common conclusion is the link to unemployment (Pritchard, 1992). Lipsedge (1995) reminds us of the significant difference in the means used to commit suicide between the genders: men notably resort to the more certain methods of asphyxiation, guns, and hanging, while women demonstrate a higher incidence of overdosing. McGovern (1996) reports finding that a history of parasuicide is a factor in 50% of subsequently successful cases.

Literature review

Aggression and violence

Philo *et al.* (1993) report the constant repetition in the media of negative and stigmatising portrayals of people with mental health problems. Reed (1997) states that serious aggression and violence is rare in the mental health population. This is very different to the messages given by media representation and subsequent public perception. Fuller Torrey (1994) reports that although the vast majority of individuals with serious mental illness are no more dangerous than the general population, there appears to be a sub-group who are presenting significant dangers highlighted by the repeated reports of inquiry into homicides caused by people with a mental illness.

Monahan & Arnold (1996) suggest that the public perception that mental illness is strongly linked to violence is a most damaging stereotype of service users in general and a serious barrier for service providers to have to negotiate.

McClelland (1995) and Vaughan & Badger (1995) remind us that the process and outcome of risk assessment is an uncertain business. However, while prediction of human behaviour is recognised to be an inaccurate art, there is an ever-growing volume of research evidence directing us towards the factors and procedures that underpin good practice.

Reed suggests that the majority of people with psychiatric diagnoses share the same risk predictors as the general population, that is, previous history of violent behaviour, age and gender factors. He states that these diagnoses become significant when specific active symptoms are present, notably command hallucinations and delusional ideas of a paranoid nature. When you add to these active symptoms the concurrent misuse of drugs and/or alcohol, the risks are significantly increased.

McClelland highlights a combination of psychiatric history, index offence, and presenting behaviour as important ingredients informing predictive ability.

Wykes *et al.* (1994) refer to additional socio-demographic factors:

- age – significant peak in 20s
- gender – more predominantly male
- ethnicity – no strong correlations for different groups, despite the frequent perception of Black men being more dangerous (more frequently sectioned, and over-represented in the secure population).

Prins (1986) argues, in relation to dangerousness, that we should not see the incidents in isolation from the context of their situation. It is both unhelpful and misleading to see people as risky individuals; rather we should see them as people reacting to risky situations.

Suicide and self-harm

This category is made more complex by inclusion in the research and literature of two different concepts: deliberate suicide attempts and non-fatal deliberate self-harm. The distinctions are more fully elaborated in Vaughan (1995).

The *Health of the Nation* targets for reducing the incidence of suicide were set in 1993 (Department of Health, 1993). These have been recently revised: *'To reduce by at least one-sixth, the death rate from suicide and undetermined injury by 2010, from a baseline at 1996'* (Department of Health, 1998).

Allen *et al.* (1997) identify the ambivalence in staff towards people presenting with deliberate self-harm. There appears to be a group of people who generate persistent fears that their parasuicide behaviour will lead on to successful suicide.

Severe self-neglect

Anecdotally, this appears to be the most frequent incidence of risk presentation, though it receives little or no research attention. People experiencing severe and enduring mental health problems are likely to be at risk of severe self-neglect. This is widely assumed to be a consequence of the common negative symptoms of schizophrenia (Bouricius, 1989; Barnes, 1994).

> ■ **Who can take responsibility in your local team or service for ensuring regular reviews are made of the research and literature on risk assessment?**

Risk assessment for whom?

With so many interested parties offering opinions and judgement on the ability of mental health services to assess the risks effectively, it is important for the clinicians to maintain a focus on which interests are, or could be, influencing their decisions:

- **the government** – needing to be responsive to media representation and its influences on public perceptions
- **the public** – fearful of the incidents which are reported and the linking of these to the policy of community care
- **the employer** – mindful to fulfil obligations set out in national guidance and legislation and also reticent to see the organisation scapegoated in the media
- **the multidisciplinary team** – needing to put into operation the policies of the organisation and wishing to avoid the scrutiny of the serious incidents inquiry

- **the clinician** – issues of self-preservation are perfectly legitimate influences on individual practice
- **service users and carers** – the people who are collectively at most risk and who should be empowered to be involved as the key central figures in the overall process of assessment. Risk assessment should not be professionalised to the point of creating a mystique that excludes the most significant people, relegating them to the role of passive recipients.

Potential impact on staff

The pressure of expectations around prediction, and subsequent fear of blame and scapegoating for failure, can lead to what Moore (1996) calls 'repetitive doubt syndrome'. Symptoms experienced by clinicians may include:

- irritability
- fatigue
- loss of morale
- premature ageing
- a deep sense of being misunderstood and abused.

Unhelpful responses to these symptoms would be:

- developing an artificial sense of certainty about decisions
- translating suspicions into definite theories
- accepting anecdotal evidence as the rule
- allowing prejudices to become accepted indicators.

Moore proposes that requirements to offset these responses would include *'humility, tolerance of doubt, and adherence to good practice through the following framework for risk assessment:*

1 *Define the behaviour to be predicted.*

2 *Distinguish between "probability" and "cost" of the behaviour.*

3 *Be aware of probable sources of error:*
   - *attributes of the person being assessed; for example, a poor informant*
   - *attributes of the assessor; for example, rigid personal values*
   - *attributes of the context; for example, agency bias towards one source.*

4 *Take into account both internal and external factors.*

5 *Check whether all necessary information has been gathered.*

6 *Identify if and when other specialists need to be involved.*

7 *Plan key interventions.*

8 *Predict the factors likely to increase or decrease future risk'.*

I would also add to this list:

9 Have an explicit understanding of what can realistically be achieved within the realms of human behaviour.

10 Take a proactive approach to individual and group support and supervision.

Monahan & Steadman (1996) use the analogy of weather forecasting to provide guidance on how to improve our abilities in risk assessment. By implication we should consider:

- shorter-term and more frequent assessments of the situation
- the importance of the local context
- efficient communication of the information to all those who need to know.

> ■ **What do you consider, at this stage, to be the mechanisms for assessing risk in your team or service?**

What are we assessing?

We are assessing:

- individual risk
- situational risk
- systems risk.

These may be stated in the assessment as:

1 The individual:
- all the factors outlined in relation to individual behaviours and cognitions, including psychiatric history and current mental state, personality and past risk behaviours
- situational context in which all previous incidents have occurred
- information about victims, where relevant.

2 The worker:
- abilities and experience for working with issues of risk (not only to be seen as a quality of professional grading)
- expertise through training, confidence, and high quality support and supervision.

3 The environment:
- physical layout of home, office, ward, such as:
  - positioning of furniture
  - clear exit routes
  - presence of potential weapons

- effects on emotional arousal, for example:
  - long waiting times
  - lack of information about situation
  - temperature extremes
  - overcrowding
  - service routine prioritised over service user needs.

4 The community:

- threats from carers, friends, neighbours
- visiting times; for example, day or night
- signs of identification; for example, carrying medication, marked vehicle
- housing estates with dangerous reputations.

5 The systems:

- inter-agency co-ordination; for example, local CPA/care management implementation
- lines of communication; for example, inter-agency agreements on confidentiality
- caseload sizes and priorities
- clinically relevant operational policies
- links with primary care, voluntary sector, and so on (as potential sources for risks arising).

Note: this is not an exhaustive list, neither will all of these points be relevant to each individual you are assessing. They offer a guide to the diversity of what may need to be assessed in any given situation or point in time.

Purpose of assessment

Risk assessment, as in the case of all good assessment, is a continuing process; it is not a one-off exercise. It is the process of gathering information from multiple sources and informants, with the focus of identifying the factors associated with an increased probability of a risk behaviour happening. It is the foundation on which to make risk decisions and formulate risk plans, through available national and local policies and procedures.

Good practice in risk assessment requires us to translate our knowledge into a clearly delineated formulation of the risks (Lipsedge, 1995). This formulation should ideally reflect aspects of individual, context and systems that may influence the potential for risks.

Format for formulation of risk

An example of how to set out this formulation is given in the accompanying **Trainers' manual**, with the risk assessment format:

- categories of risk; for example, severe self-neglect, violence, self-harm
- named individual; that is, the service user

- potential situation; that is, the context in which risk may occur
- other people; that is, those who may influence the level of risk
- thought processes; for example, command hallucinations, or acting on delusional beliefs
- behaviour patterns; for example, use of alcohol or drugs
- experiences; for example, medication side effects influencing non-compliance
- early warning signs; for example, changing behaviour patterns or routines
- people to be informed; that is, others in the care planning meeting
- potential crisis responses; that is, appropriate access to local crisis services.

The addition of the following predictions will complete the picture, but they are difficult to quantify with any accuracy. It is important to present these as guides, not as absolutes:

- the level of risk:
  - high
  - medium
  - low
  - no risk: a difficult statement to make with certainty
- to whom:
  - who are the previous victims?
  - who are the potential victims?
  - who are the specifically identified victims?
  - why are/were these people victims?
- in what timescale:
  - imminent danger can be in minutes or hours, and may be sustained for a period of days
  - planned intent may be immediate, or a risk over days/weeks
  - depending on the sustainability of the supporting risk factors
  - some assessments of medium or low risk may be stated with reasonable confidence across a period of months, providing the factors sustaining this prediction are made explicit; it is reasonable to expect such statements to be agreed in a care-programme approach plan.

Such a formulation provides the link to and basis for the function of risk management (discussed in the next section).

Methods of assessments

The means by which individuals gather information and conduct their assessment are many and varied. The most significant factors are:

- access to the relevant information
- time for gathering, discussing and analysing the information.

The methods used are:

- access to past records, from all relevant sources

- self-reports at interviews

- observing discrepancies between verbal and non-verbal cues

- reports from significant others/formal and informal discussions, such as:
  - carers, friends, relatives
  - other team members/other teams
  - other statutory or voluntary sector mental health agencies
  - police, probation, courts

- rating scales and/or descriptive reports

- intuitive gut reactions (vital clues, but not easily documented)

- recognising repeating patterns of behaviour.

It is not always a solitary exercise, although initial data collection, interviews and observations may be the responsibility of one or two people. It requires perseverance and persistence to gain the relevant information, and detailed multidisciplinary discussion to organise and evaluate it. Assessment is as much about telephone conversations and written requests as it is about translating the information into a coherent plan of action.

> ■ **What local mechanisms are used/needed to ensure a consistent level of competence across staff members in the application of assessment methods?**

Frequency of assessment

Risk assessment is a function in which we constantly engage, both in our personal and working lives. Every choice we make involves risk; every action we take involves risk. Interactions with others always involve some degree of assessment of risk, based on our evaluation of physical presentation, verbal communication and pattern of behaviour. We do not usually formalise the assessment, and quite often do not even consciously acknowledge that we are assessing risks.

The more detailed and formal risk assessments will take place usually in the context of:

- the routine formal care planning procedures, as locally agreed; for example, the six-monthly review under the CPA (three-monthly for Supervision Register requirements)

- the extraordinary circumstances where significant risk factors, or a recognised previous pattern leading to risk behaviours, are identified by any of the people involved in the individual management plan

- a request from the service user.

Any of these situations should trigger the combined efforts, knowledge, and expertise of the relevant people who contribute to the specific risk assessment and management plan.

```
CASE EXAMPLE
```

Maria is a woman in her mid-30s with a 20-year history of self-harming and suicide attempts. Self-harming behaviours and expressing the view 'that she would be better off dead' are daily occurrences. As such, they are recorded and monitored in the CMHT client notes, but do not in themselves constitute a change from the norm that would require a full multidisciplinary risk assessment.

When Maria begins to develop statements of planned intent, or uses methods of self-harming that differ from the identified pattern, the circumstances are sufficiently altered to require a full risk assessment involving Maria and all others involved in her support network.

Clinical considerations

Risk factors for aggression and violence

Based on Lipsedge (1995), the following is a succinct summary of important factors in relation to the prediction of violence:

- antecedents:
  - a previous history of violence
  - personality development (listed separately)
- diagnosis:
  - schizophrenia, specifically with paranoid features
  - morbid jealousy and erotomania
  - illicit drug and/or alcohol misuse
- social or domestic factors:
  - loss of family support
  - deterioration in personal relationships
- clinical:
  - declared intentions and attitudes to previous and potential victims
  - threats of violence
  - presence of active symptoms, including delusions (especially regarding poisoning and sexual matters), passivity experiences, command hallucinations, jealousy, depression, and anger outbursts
  - signs and symptoms of relapse
- management:
  - loss of contact with mental health services
  - poor adherence with medication

> ■ **How can you apply a general list to the individual clinical situations you will encounter in your own practice?**

Personality factors

The following need to be investigated on an individual basis, rather than assumed to be significant in most cases:

- cultural/sub-cultural values in relation to the use of aggression and violence
- parental attitudes and child-rearing behaviours
- repeated exposure to aggression and violence
- failure to learn delay in gratification of wants
- failure to develop alternative strategies, other than the use of aggression and violence
- taking offence easily
- impulsive behaviours
- inability to cope with stress and frustration
- unresolved conflicts from previous rejections
- anxiety about losing control
- hostile response to authority
- inferiority complex
- continual denial of aggressive behaviours
- lack of remorse
- obsession with bizarre events or sadistic fantasies.

> ■ **From where might you access some of the above information in your local team or service?**

Assessing imminent dangers

Faulk (1994) identifies a range of factors that we need to be aware of when the signs of aggression are increasing:

- current mental state
- state of emotional arousal
- degree of hostility
- overt or covert expression of an intention to harm others
- recent behaviour
- past dangerous behaviour
- social tensions
- uncooperative with treatment.

Further physical warning signs may include:

- clenched fists
- walking briskly/pacing
- throwing objects
- exaggerated responses to annoyance
- pressured and/or loud speech
- rigid muscle tension
- verbal threats
- invading personal space
- disinhibition.

Note: any significant change from the normal for a specific individual should be considered seriously. The accuracy of any one of the above as a predictor is questionable and should be clearly considered within the context of the situation.

CASE EXAMPLE

Mitchell is a man in his early 30s with an identified dual diagnosis of schizophrenia and multiple drug abuse. He was raised in and out of foster care, having experienced periods of violence from and between his own family members. He has no clear role models of acceptable behaviour patterns in his childhood and adolescence, quickly resorting to violence and aggression to gain what he wants. Mitchell denies he has a mental illness, or any need for prescribed medication. He has brief periods of insight into his behaviour, which is linked to the abuse of drugs when he has settled down on periods of admission to the in-patient unit. However, on discharge he rapidly resorts to familiar networks and behaviours, with few alternative options offered to him.

Suicide and self-harm

The most significant variable across the literature can be summarised as:

- personal characteristics:
  - gender component (more females attempt, more males succeed)
  - age-related component (higher rates with increasing age)
  - cultural components (for example, Asian women; young males)
  - marital status/disruption (higher in single, widowed, separated, and divorced)
  - employment status (higher in unemployed)
  - family history of suicide, increases risk potential
  - social network development (higher in socially isolated people)
  - recent adverse life events

- health characteristics:
  - terminal illness
  - major physical illness or disability
  - psychiatric history, diagnoses indicated above
  - previous history of suicide attempts
  - alcohol or drug misuse
  - time of hospital discharge
  - persistent sleep disruption

- characteristics of plan:
  - definite statements of planned intent
  - degree of irreversibility of plan
  - absence of proximity of others (in stated plan)
  - preparation (for example, hoarding tablets, settling financial affairs)
  - access to means (for example, medication, carbon monoxide)
  - perceived absence of, or unwillingness to use, support systems

- intangibles:
  - strength of emotional ties to significant others; expressing real or perceived feelings of worthlessness in the eyes of others will increase the risk
  - trust in the clinician; the working relationship may form a significant bond to provide some source of hope in an otherwise hopeless situation
  - likely effectiveness of treatment; this will depend on the individual's previous experiences of prescribed treatment interventions, or openness to persuasion about the potential benefits of different ideas
  - potential transference and counter-transference; depending on feelings released in either service user or practitioner, through unconscious links to previous experiences
  - others?

CASE EXAMPLE

Joyce is a woman in her mid-50s with a 30-year history of being diagnosed with psychotic depression. She has had numerous short hospital admissions, with follow-up out-patient appointments and prescriptions of oral and depot medications. While reasonably compliant with medications, she felt many different types had been tried but she still became ill.

Joyce was discharged from hospital last week, with an appointment for the clinic next week. Her 26-year-old son was killed in a car accident two months ago and she was told a year ago that she had advanced signs of osteoporosis. Yesterday Joyce's husband came home from work to find her dead on the bathroom floor. She had taken all of her tablets given to her by the ward on discharge.

Deliberate self-harm

Deliberate self-harm constitutes a deliberate non-fatal act, done in the knowledge that it was potentially harmful (Vaughan, 1995). Some admit they are ambivalent about the outcome or unthinking of the consequences. It is difficult to quantify the incidence of deliberate self-harm, as not all cases come into contact with mental health services. They are not a homogeneous group of people, though there are some clear indications of people more likely to behave in this way:

- younger people (15–25) have highest rates
- women have twice the rate of men
- social deprivation and unemployment
- single parent families, or other family problems
- acute emotional upsets, such as a row with a key person
- drug and/or alcohol misuse
- history of impulsive acts of self-harming.

 For many people this act is an expression of extreme distress, not an act of manipulation or attention-seeking; it frequently indicates a previous, or on-going, experience as a victim of serious abuse.

Severe self-neglect

The sub-categories of self-neglect to be considered in the assessment of risk are:

- the development of serious physical disability or illness, as a result of neglect
- a relapse into a serious mental state that would endanger general health and well-being, clearly identified as caused by neglect of self and/or treatment
- the development of a serious environmental health problem that may endanger the individual, carers or other visitors.

The factors to consider in a risk assessment may be:

- a previous history of severe mental illness resulting in episodes of severe self-neglect, including environmental health problems through deteriorating condition of accommodation
- progressively deteriorating physical condition, denied by the individual in the face of other evidence
- repeated non-compliance with treatment and/or support consistent with evidence of self-neglect
- a progressive denial and neglect of personal appearance, hygiene and daily living skills
- the hoarding of rubbish and persistent neglect of rotting food
- a denial of danger from malfunctioning appliances, such as a cooker or fire
- the disconnection of essential utilities: water, gas or electricity, as a direct consequence of neglect and denial
- leaving home with doors unlocked and open

(Morgan, 1998).

It would be dangerous to assume that any one of these factors alone is sufficient to declare severe neglect to be present as a high level of risk. It is much more clear if a combination of a number of these factors exists and is supported by evidence that they arise out of denial or avoidance of expected *normal* social controls and limits on personal behaviour. Furthermore, this should not be seen as an exhaustive list, but as an indicator of the directions severe self-neglect may more commonly take.

CASE EXAMPLE

Jake is a man in his mid-30s with a 10-year history of schizophrenia. He denies that he has an illness, refuses all offers of prescribed medication and spends most of his weekly money on cannabis. His one-bedroom flat has only broken furniture, he sleeps on a dirty floor, generally fully clothed. He has a very poor diet, usually the cheapest take-away food he can find, and occasionally visits a soup-kitchen he knows from his early experience of the homeless circuit.

Jake will occasionally answer the door to a visiting community mental health worker and apologises for the condition of the flat, stating he will tidy up 'tomorrow'. He denies the need for help, despite his electricity and gas supplies being cut off. He denies that he is being victimised by other local residents, despite racist graffiti daubed on his front door. Jake has recently suggested his persistent chesty cough may be bronchitis and that he will go to his GP soon.

Recording the assessment

Descriptive formats

Detailed and complex discussions and deliberations of the continuing assessment process require a format for recording. While requiring a degree of standardisation in the format, an additional degree of flexibility is needed to account for the individuality of all service users and hence their assessments. The format should reflect quantitative and qualitative assessment information.

The format included in the **Trainer's manual** for group training purposes has been developed and tested through workshop situations, to meet these requirements of flexibility and individuality. The sections are:

1 Categories of risk identified, for example:
- aggression and violence
- suicide and self-harm
- severe self-neglect
- exploitation by others.

2 Detail any historical information that may indicate the potential for risk, for example:
- personal
- family
- forensic
- social
- interpersonal.

3 Detail any health-related factors that may contribute to the potential for risk for example:
- psychiatric symptoms
- personality factors
- physical disabilities
- substance abuse.

4 What risks has the client experienced from others, such as:
- carers, relatives or neighbours
- broader community
- racial or culturally motivated
- service providers.

5 Are there any factors that indicate preferred staff allocation, for instance:
- danger to women
- intimidated by men
- type of therapeutic approach
- need for two workers.

6 What environmental factors may contribute risks, for example:
- housing estates with poor reputations
- presence of others posing potential risks, such as other drug users
- visiting out-of-hours or after dark
- imposing or unwelcoming service base that could contribute to emotional arousal.

7 Are there any organisation/system factors to be considered, such as:
- problems of service co-ordination
- inter-professional/inter-agency differences of philosophy or approach
- waiting lists/delays
- reaction to officials; for example, hostile to authority.

8 Is there any current evidence to suggest planned intent to engage in risk-related behaviour?

9 Is there an immediate need for more detailed risk assessment?

This format aims to cover all the areas listed earlier under **What are we assessing?** (See page 27).

Particular attention is drawn to the inclusion of service users' experiences of risk from others, which are needed to make this a more balanced and accurate assessment of all the relevant risks. Flexibility is offered through the space to write comments on most of the form, while still achieving a degree of standardisation through the structure of the form.

This format should also serve to remind people that accurate assessment arises from detailed discussion with all the relevant people involved; it is not restricted to a single professional observation and rating.

> ■ **What do you consider to be the pros and cons of using a descriptive format for risk assessments in your local team or service?**

Rating scales, schedules and objective measures

Attempts to develop instruments for the objective assessment of risk have been researched for several decades. In the US, the most ambitious is the MacArthur Risk Assessment Study, a longitudinal multisite study of approximately 1000 people. This work, led by Monahan & Steadman (1994), commenced in 1989 and utilises a battery of research and clinical tools to assess:

- personal factors (such as personality or cognition)

- historical development factors (for example, family, psychiatric, criminal histories)

- situational factors (such as stress, social support, means)

- clinical factors (for example, psychotic symptoms, activities of daily living, substance misuse, treatment).

The hypothesis is essentially that if clinicians can be supported to make objective, impersonal and unbiased assessments using rigorously tested procedures with good predictive value, outcomes from risk assessments will be greatly improved and public confidence will be enhanced, with decreased doubt and scrutiny.

In the UK, there are examples of the use of rating scales and schedules in risk assessment (Feaviour et al., 1995). However, there is still a strong backing of descriptive clinical judgement and decision making.

Examples of scales and schedules currently in use in the UK are:
- aggression and violence in psychoses (Wykes et al., 1994):
  - Overt Aggression Scale
  - Modified Overt Aggression Scale
  - Scale for the Assessment of Aggression and Agitated Behaviours
  - Aggression Risk Profile
  - Buss-Durkee Hostility Inventory
  - Novaco Anger Inventory
  - Over controlled Hostility Scale
  - Blackburn's Assessment Schedules
- suicide risk in psychoses (Hawton, 1994):
  - Risk Estimator for Suicide
  - Hopelessness Scale
  - Scale for Suicidal Ideation
  - Scale for Assessing Suicide Risk of Attempted Suicides
  - Suicide Intent Scale
  - Risk of Repetition Scale.

It is more common to see examples of the above tools used in the application of research studies, rather than in the routine clinical practice of many mental health workers. Their use in clinical services may be hampered by the perception that all busy clinicians should be carrying out an extensive battery of research and psychological tests on all their clients as a routine practice. Time does not permit such a luxury and any such expectation is likely to be met with unhelpful resistance.

It is essential that clinicians are at least aware of these scales and measures and of who has the requisite expertise to conduct them in a clinically relevant way. Their use is more likely to be indicated when a need for a more detailed comprehensive risk assessment is shown, through the more commonly used screening and descriptive formats. This is the stage when the multidisciplinary team will determine the need for more specialist assessment information and to whom to refer in the local service for this function.

Screening measures

While still dependent on information seeking, interview and observation, a mechanism is desirable for screening who should continue on current plans and who requires more comprehensive assessment. In order to make this slightly more objective we require a form of rating or measurement on which to base the next stage of our interventions.

A template for such a tool would need sections for the different risk categories identified and further sub-sections for significant factors. The content of such a tool would differ in the context of local services and personnel, so the following can only offer broad directions and minimum standards, which would need to be developed more specifically for the team/service's needs:

1 Aggression and violence:
- repeat patterns of behaviour
- expressed wish to harm others
- drug/alcohol use
- contact with potential victims
- build up of aggression
- current mental state
- non-compliance with formal/informal supports
- others

2 Suicide:
- intended plans
- current mental state
- perceived hopelessness/helplessness
- drug/alcohol use
- recent life events
- levels of distress/coping strategies
- access to means
- others

3 Severe self-neglect:
- mental health
- physical health
- environmental health
- connection/use of utilities
- activities of daily living
- others

4 Exploitation:
- emotional
- physical
- financial
- sexual
- ethnic/cultural
- social network
- others

5 Other categories of risk?

When the template has been developed in detail you may wish to put score values, or ranking systems, into the measures. Alternatively, a simple yes/no or tick box method may serve to highlight the needs for more detailed formal risk assessment. The Weighted Risk Indicator, developed by Worthing Priority Care NHS Trust, incorporates a system of measures and has the desired characteristics of being rigorously validated against a range of research-based assessments (contact the service direct for further details and discussion).

■ **How could a screening tool for risk assessment be developed in your team or service? If one already exists, how do you now rate its effectiveness?**

Current assessment tools

Tools for recording assessment that are currently in use by different UK clinical services include:

RAMAS (Risk, Assessment, Management and Audit System)

This includes a detailed risk assessment checklist, with items covering historical and current behaviours in relation to the major identified categories of risk. Assessor is required to tick a box for each risk marker present, with one line to detail any further comments.

CANVAS (Clinical Assessment of Need: Violence Appraisal System)

This is a detailed tool, linked to the assessment and management of violence, and developed through three modules:

1   Summary of history of violence against other people; set out in columns to record dates of incidents, source of information, type of violence, and so on.

2   Risk assessment schedule; with detailed risk factor lists separated out into male and female sub-schedules.

3   Risk of violence management plan; including recording management issues and management options, and an outline risk plan.

Detailed instructions are set out on the reverse of the module sheets, which give guidance on their use and on conducting interviews to elicit information.

The British Psychological Society (BPS) CORE (Centre for Clinical Outcomes Research and Effectiveness) Guide to Risk Assessment

This tool includes an assessment summary identifying the major categories of risk and the relationship to locally implemented guidance and legislation for a sample Supervision Register.

The risk profile combines tick-box answers to identify risk factors and descriptive accounts of risk history and current warning signs. Sources of information are usefully documented and the information is linked to a relapse and management plan.

Mental Health Risk Needs Matrix (Berkshire Social Services)

This matrix consists of rows to represent the nature of needs and columns to represent the degree of risk. This tool attempts to give brief descriptions of the severity of needs in relation to safety, mental health, physical health, social and emotional development and social interaction/community involvement. The boxes within the matrix also record a form of numerical weighting for the degrees of risk identified.

Barnsley Mental Health Register (Barnsley Community and Priority Services NHS Trust)

This is a detailed practitioner guide that outlines service integration, the CPA and gives a definition of severe need and a risk assessment indicator. The subsequent register risk assessment identifies 33 rated items, leading to a scoring chart linked to CPA tiers and a basic recording of identified need and agreed action.

Weighted Risk Indicator (Worthing Priority Care NHS Trust)

This tool includes three separate indicators (suicide/neglect/violence) each with 15 weighted risk markers. Scores can be compared with categories of low, medium and high in each indicator. The tool has been rigorously validated against a range of research-based assessments.

General Assessment of Risk (North Derbyshire Social Services)

This is a written guide to the assessment and management of risks in the three major categories of suicide, severe self-neglect and violence, which lists general indicators, statistically based factors, and indications towards the process of monitoring and managing risks.

Birmingham Drug Services Client Assessment, Risk Assessment and Care Planning

This tool includes a detailed schedule of questions across 16 personal and health-related domains. Some six domains are identified as contributing to the assessment of risks and the answers have accompanying scores which feed into a screening framework of no/low/medium/high risk. A further risk assessment summary record offers the opportunity to describe the identified risk and method of risk reduction for each of the domains.

The above tools are included for descriptive purposes and are not critically evaluated in this text. They give an indication of the different styles of approach currently being adopted in the UK. Scepticism about the ability of scales and rated schedules to represent fully the complexity of the risk assessment process hides potential values that such instruments may offer to busy clinical services. I would propose that the categories and lists identified through such instruments could offer:

- a screening mechanism for the appropriateness of referrals to a service (when used in conjunction with other criteria; for example, disability, diagnosis, complexity of needs)

- a measure that draws attention to definite potentials for risks, which then require further investigation

- a standard measure which may be repeated at regular intervals to give a quantifiable representation of change over a period of time (giving valuable feedback for service users, workers and managers alike).

CHAPTER

THREE   RISK MANAGEMENT

Introduction

Clinical risk management will largely occur through the interpretation and implementation of agreed individual care plans. The development of a comprehensive and individualised care plan will relate to the broad range of effective treatment, rehabilitation and support services provided at the current level of clinical knowledge. Research evidence is available worldwide to support the effectiveness of a range of clinical interventions with people experiencing severe and enduring mental health problems. Some of these include:

- intensive case management within the context of a comprehensive range of community support services (Dvoskin & Steadman, 1994)

- assertive outreach, as the preferred method of service delivery (McGrew *et al.*, 1995)

- early detection of warning signs (Jackson & Birchwood, 1996)

- flexible crisis intervention strategies (Phelan *et al.*, 1997).

Clinical interventions should be offered in conjunction with:

- behavioural family interventions

- medical treatments

- practical help with:
  - housing
  - finances
  - employment opportunities
  - daily living skills.

 It should be understood that the engagement of a trusting working relationship and delivery of effective treatment and support will offer the greatest hope of risk management — largely through a preventative rather than a reactive approach.

There will still be occasions when identified risks occur, or increase, even with the application of treatment and rehabilitation interventions. On these occasions, the management of risk becomes an amalgamation of practical interventions taken within the context of administrative procedures, with the aims of:

- helping individuals to avoid risky situations

- helping the individual to deal effectively with their own risk potential

- detecting the early warning signs and taking appropriate actions, through clear procedures, when things start going wrong.

The three areas that require immediate attention by all individuals, teams and organisations are:

- procedures — agreed and more clearly adhered to
- plans — developed on the basis of quality information
- common sense — so easily lost sight of by people who consider risk management to be the domain of a few 'experts'.

These considerations are greatly enhanced by placing the first priority on engaging a trusting working relationship between all the relevant people:

- service user and service practitioner
- carer and service practitioner
- service user/carer and the broader mental health service
- between service practitioners within services
- between service agencies.

Literature review

The emerging themes from the literature on risk management are:

- risk behaviours will always occur; risk *elimination* is not a reasonable expectation
- the consequences are tragic for all concerned
- effective identification and management of risks can achieve risk *minimisation*.

Vincent (1997) states that risk management was initially seen as a means of controlling the volume of medical negligence litigation; but it is subsequently developing as a quality initiative for clinically addressing potential harmful outcomes for service users.

Roy (1997) states that risk management is *'the identification and planned response to negative events that occur during the provision of clinical care and can lead to litigation'*.

Chubb (1997) reflects a more positive outlook, stating that *'the identification and management of risk is integral to the provision of high standards of patient care and is the responsibility of every single employee'*.

Manthorpe *et al.* (1995) state that badly managed risk can damage the welfare of individuals, families and communities whereas well managed risk can increase the quality of life for the same range of people, as well as significantly contributing to the morale and confidence of staff.

> ■ **Are you aware of any local service definitions or interpretations of risk management?**

Procedural context

The parameters for establishing a multidisciplinary approach to risk management are embedded in the range of guidance and legislation presented during the 1990s, the most notable examples being:

- Care programme approach, 1991
- Supervision Registers, 1994
- After-care Under Supervision (Supervised Discharge), 1996.

Care programme approach

While the CPA is undoubtedly concerned with developing the broad range of good practice in identifying and planning co-ordinated care for people experiencing severe and enduring mental health problems, it is not solely concerned with issues of risk. However, a distinct obligation within the administrative procedures of the CPA is not only to assess risk but to ensure this is accompanied by a clear risk management plan. It is recognised that risks are not static, and thus the plan will need to be regularly reviewed and updated in response to events (Department of Health, 1995; Reed, 1997).

The principles of the CPA are:

- specialist psychiatric services should be provided through effective inter-agency working in multidisciplinary teams
- the CPA is to apply to all people accepted by specialist psychiatric services
- users and carers must be actively involved in the process
- the CPA is an *approach*, not a prescription rigidly directing local services.

The main elements of the CPA are:

- systematic arrangements for assessing the health and social care needs of people accepted by specialist psychiatric services
- formulation of a care plan
- appointment of a named key worker to maintain close contact and monitor care
- regular review and changes to the care plan when necessary (at least every six months).

The CPA is a tiered approach reflecting the complexity of individual needs, only one aspect of which will be risk. However, a number of training requests to the Sainsbury Centre for Mental Health have highlighted organisations requirements to focus the assessment and management of risk within the context of the local implementation of the CPA. The broad considerations of risk management, within detailed care plans, will be addressed later in this section, and some of the systems risks identified through CPA practice will be considered in **Chapter Four: Service organisation**.

■ **How does the process of risk management fit within your local service agreements on CPA implementation?**

Supervision Registers

Commonly regarded as a sub-register within the CPA, the Supervision Register is more singularly focused on the identification and management of risk. The NHS Executive (1994) outlines the need to clearly delineate people with a severe mental illness who may present a serious risk of:

- aggression and violence
- suicide and self-harm
- severe self-neglect.

Consideration for inclusion on the register will be part of the pre-discharge meeting. The decision on inclusion will be the responsibility of the Responsible Medical Officer, in consultation with the multi-disciplinary team. Inclusion should automatically identify a greater level of need/service priority, requiring a detailed multidisciplinary risk assessment.

Inclusion on the Supervision Register does not necessarily bring with it any additional resources for risk management within the care plan, but does require more frequent reviews (three-monthly). This should enable a regular update of the plan, and also frequent consideration of possible removal from the register where risks are deemed to be reasonably managed.

■ **How does the implementation of the Supervision Register in your service support the clinical management of risk?**

After-care under supervision

Initiated through the *Mental Health (Patients in the Community) Act 1995*, this piece of legislation is primarily concerned with the community management of people thought to pose serious risks. It is initiated within the hospital setting for detained patients, not subject to Home Office restrictions, prior to their discharge. It lengthens the period of extended leave to six months, but with no provisions for compulsory treatment in the community. A nominated person has to agree to become supervisor for an individual service user under this legislation. The defined powers suggest that:

- the patient should live in a particular place
- the patient should attend a particular place at set times for medical treatments, occupation, education or training
- the supervisor, or person authorised by them, should be allowed access to the patient at his or her place of residence
- the supervisor, or person authorised by them, may convey the patient to places specified above.

No powers exist to impose treatment, occupation, education or training, at the places the patient is required to attend.

Effective implementation of this legislation has been largely hampered by a significant contradiction:

- the revised code of practice accompanying the Act suggests that these requirements will need substantial agreement by the patient and carer to be successful

- without such agreement they will be difficult to achieve, yet many people who will agree with risk management, and broader care plans, are less likely to need the extra weight of this legislation
- those for whom agreement is more of a problem are going to be less likely to engage and trust service practitioners who use the implied powers in the legislation.

■ **How has supervised discharge been received and implemented in your local services, and what additional support does it offer to risk management?**

Procedural skills

The procedural skills of risk management occur in the context of a positive and constructive care planning process. The key worker, or care co-ordinator, needs to ensure that:

- all people who have a reason to be involved in the process are kept informed and updated
- all the relevant people, specifically the service users and carers, have the complexities of the organisational procedures clearly explained to them, so they are able to feel included as an important part of the overall care plan, and the management of all risks within it.

The process, envisaged through local implementation of the national guidance and legislation, should be functional and practical. There is a requirement to hold multidisciplinary meetings on a frequent basis, to draw up and review an individual care plan. Where relevant, a risk management plan will form a part of this care planning process. To achieve the desired aims effectively, certain characteristics can be identified for the organisation of the required formal meeting:

- a clear agenda
- an independent chair (the key worker cannot reasonably be expected to chair, minute, and contribute their own information and that of others not present — not without one or all functions failing)
- an independent minute-taker ensuring all key people are present, or at least have their views and contributions clearly represented
- clear decisions for the care plan (including risk management plans) are made.

Practitioners need to feel confident in their skills for including the service users and their carers in the whole process by ensuring:

- the procedural arrangements, and the reasoning for them, are clearly explained in language that is understandable to the ordinary lay person
- the procedural arrangements are applied in a flexible manner, again so as not to exclude the very people who need to feel at the centre of the whole process of care planning (including risk management) — the service users and carers.

This latter point may be achieved, in some instances, by:

- addressing the way meetings are structured, so as to primarily meet the needs of the service user above those of the service providers — not many people feel comfortable with the standard ward round format for meetings, with larger groups of people discussing the service user

- meetings could be split into sub-meetings, jointly contributing to the total CPA process, with the key worker as the common figure in all the separate sub-meetings

- effective care planning, and risk management, requires sufficient time for relevant discussions with all the key people, to elicit the clear plans

- empowerment of service users and carers through involvement.

CASE EXAMPLE

Michael is a man in his mid-30s who has held very strong feelings of rejection throughout his life. In recent years he has felt rejected by the mental health services that he assumes should be meeting his needs. A complexity of factors, involving his social network and the services, have led Michael to react by violent means. Following a period of time in prison awaiting sentencing, the mental health and criminal justice systems are challenged with a need to re-engage Michael's trust in order to initiate a new plan of care.

The CPA meeting has to be creatively negotiated, as Michael will not sit in a room with some of the potentially large group of people involved in his care package. Each six-monthly CPA meeting is now re-negotiated across a series of meetings:

1 Michael will initially meet with the CMHT key worker and the probation officer.

2 Staff (including the consultant psychiatrist).

3 The CMHT key worker meets again with Michael to discuss any new information/ideas arising from meeting **2**.

4 The CMHT key worker telephones the probation officer to outline the outcomes of meetings **2** and **3** and to negotiate any further differences that may have arisen between mental health and criminal justice systems.

The key worker fulfils an essential co-ordinating role across all negotiations, ensuring Michael is kept at the centre of the process. This accepts his wishes not to have to attend a potentially damaging and negative, large meeting, in the presence of people to whom he would not feel able to express his views constructively.

■ **What guidance do you have, in your local service, for implementing the procedural arrangements of formal meetings?**

Clinical team procedures

In addition to the local implementation of the above procedures from the guidance and legislation, individual clinical teams will have a certain degree of autonomy (within policy guidance of their employing organisation) to implement their own risk management procedures. Some examples of these are:

- team meetings:
  - considering referrals (the process of risk management, as with risk assessment, should begin at the point of initial referral)
  - allocation and assessment procedures (should more than one worker be involved?)
  - team workload/caseload priorities (effective risk management requires adequate resourcing)

- team policies for:
  - home visiting
  - staffing levels and cover
  - office diary of staff whereabouts
  - crisis/emergency responses

- support and supervision:
  - regular individual, team and group supervision should be encouraged
  - to include proactive focus on risk management issues within the care planning process

- communication of information:
  - note-keeping and documentation
  - internal hand-over
  - links with external agencies
  - clarity on issues of confidentiality
  - use of clinical audit, for example to provide information on numbers and types of incidents of risk, such as suicide

- health and safety:
  - reviewing the risks posed by the building(s)
  - reviewing procedures on a regular basis

- priority for risk management in staff training.

■ **Can you identify the procedures that your team or service have in place to support effective risk management and what gaps need to be addressed?**

Managing risk behaviours

The following three phases apply to all aspects of effective treatment, rehabilitation and support. In the context of this handbook they are applied more specifically to risk management. All people who may be required to exercise risk management procedures, plans or techniques need to be aware of, and differentiate between:

- preventative approaches to help manage their own risk behaviours, through:
  - education about causes and/or early detection
  - access to flexible support
  - development of skills and/or techniques for coping
- managing risk behaviours (for example, aggression or self-harming) when they are occurring, through:
  - direct treatment
  - diffusion strategies
  - crisis responses
- management of supported learning, after a risk (for example, violence or suicide) has occurred, through:
  - counselling, open to all parties involved
  - accurate incident reporting and serious incidents committees
  - appropriateness of pressing charges, with relevant support.

Examples of potential strategies

Before an event

This strategy works with people in a positive and proactive manner, based on the assumption that optimising treatment and rehabilitation efforts will support progress, with less need for managing the real outcomes of risk. Examples of effective service delivery would include:

- intensive clinical case management approaches
- assertive outreach as the flexible method of working
- engaging trusting working relationships
- working with service user strengths, wishes and priorities
- comprehensive health and social care interventions
- supportive counselling
- systematic monitoring of mental health and medication adherence
- anger management techniques
- cognitive behavioural approaches
- social skills training
- goal setting and problem solving
- controlling emotional arousal
- work with significant others or social networks (within the bounds of confidentiality).

During an event

At a time of personal crisis, relapse of a medical condition, or an incident (violence to self or others), we need to have some recognised and effective measures with which to make an immediate response. Examples should reflect a balance of the recognised effective treatment options, and more immediate emergency procedures:

- evidence-based crisis intervention responses, for example:
  - medication management
  - negotiation skills, to compromise on potential developments and outcomes
  - practical help, to achieve some immediate positive rewards
  - respite, for the person most in need/amenable
- setting clear ground rules and limits, with explicit consequences for specific behaviours
- focus on the aim of helping the client to maintain control of their experience
- monitor clinical symptoms, for example with recognised tools such as Brief Psychiatric Rating Scale
- determine the need for a formal psychiatric assessment under the Mental Health Act
- encourage discussion of recognised signs and patterns
- problem-solving and coping strategies
- forensic assessments, when appropriate
- calling for emergency services, when appropriate
- offering help and support to those in need other than the service user.

After an event

Crises and risk incidents (such as violence, self-harm, suicide, or removal from a situation of environmental health hazard) have an impact on all those involved and offer opportunities to learn from real experiences. Strategies are required to ensure people are supported and lessons are identified:

- a learning experience that should be talked through with the service user, as a part of a process of psycho-education, or for its contribution to the refining of early warning signs/relapse signature
- staff members should be encouraged to talk through the experience with their supervisor/manager (including consideration of the potential difficulties of a worker having to re-face a perpetrator of distressing risk, continuing in the role of key worker)
- discussing experiences in the larger staff group, when the person(s) involved are ready to do so, as a learning exercise for the whole team
- an opportunity for the service to assess the causal relationships and the potential consequences for risk policy and procedures.

It is important to extend the same rights and opportunities to service users and carers, where applicable.

■ **What skills, abilities and resources are available in your local team or service to implement the above range of strategies?**

Clinical strategies

The primary emphasis should remain with effective treatment and support, but with clearly articulated mechanisms for responding to assessed risks, as agreed in the multidisciplinary team meeting. The overall effectiveness of the care plan will depend on all those involved knowing and performing their clinical, therapeutic and supportive roles:

- agreed frequency and places of contacts with the service user

- agreed professional/non-professional interventions — medical, psychosocial, practical

- contacts with others in the service user's support network; for example, carers and friends (within bounds of confidentiality)

- liaison and effective communication of information, between all those who need to know (generally all the people who are involved in the CPA meeting, relevant line managers and clinical colleagues).

In the event of assessed risks developing, the following approaches are examples of management strategies that may be used with different risk categories.

Aggression and violence

- use of open discussion is the primary approach

- allow plenty of time; sustaining anger can be difficult, so leaving the client well alone could be the safest initial step

- encourage expression of feelings through open questions, in a non-confrontational and non-judgmental manner

- as acute reactions subside, switch to a problem-solving approach, with open questions and alternative solutions

- role-model calm, non-verbal messages, but be cautious about initiating touching too soon as it may be construed as invasion of personal space or cultural norms

- if verbal aggression is directed at you, maintain a calm pace to your voice, offering options to deflect or compromise the aggression

- threats towards you should be assessed for immediacy and realistic opportunity; do not be overwhelmed by their apparent seriousness if it is not likely to happen immediately

- if threats are assessed to be immediate and likely to be acted upon, leave and seek help; do not retaliate with counter-threats

- trained breakaway techniques may be used, when necessary

- control and restraint procedures are a last option, to be used only if required by the situation

CASE EXAMPLE

Colin is pacing his flat, in a very agitated condition — restless, talkative and expressing threatening warnings that people in the mental health services will suffer the consequences of their destruction of his life over the last 20 years. You are on a home visit alone; you are aware that he has seriously attacked a ward charge nurse ten years ago; any attempt to engage discussion on the content of his threats only results in fuelling his anger — he raises his voice, denies the validity of any opinions other than his own and declares his intention to go to the psychiatric out-patient department to 'blow it up'.

CASE EXAMPLE/Continued:

You assess the immediate danger to yourself to be lowered if you actively listen by demonstrating your attention to him, without passing any comment or questioning his thinking. You are aware of the need to re-assess this situation minute-by-minute and to be aware of your immediate escape route. It takes time to allow Colin to express his anger and threats, but you feel it is better to stay with the situation, in the hope that it will help him to exhaust his anger for the present time. You assess Colin's ability to 'blow up' the out-patient department as minimal at present (though not necessarily outside the real potential of his abilities). But you feel he has the capability of causing threats and a violent incident in his current mental state. You decide to wait your chance, when the anger has subsided sufficiently, to explore alternative options for dealing with his anger, for example:

- increasing the immediate availability of meetings with you

- making a planned joint visit, with you, to the out-patient department

- Colin going to stay temporarily with a trusted close friend (who has helped him through previous bouts of extreme anger)

- arranging an admission in the medium-term to an alcohol detoxification unit that he has previously found helpful.

In this instance Colin went to stay temporarily with a relative away from his usual area of residence.

Suicidal ideas and self-harming behaviour

- deal directly with the ideas, through:
  - open questioning, to encourage full expression of what is currently being experienced
  - active listening, through verbal cues and/or non-verbal cues, as appropriate
  - empathic understanding, by offering reflective comments on what is being said to you

- assess for immediacy and realistic potential

- an initial telephone discussion should quickly be followed by face-to-face contact

- keep the client fully involved in all aspects of treatment, through:
  - discussions and supportive counselling
  - explanations and psycho-education
  - continual questioning to elicit changes in urgency

- tailor problem solving to the personal strengths, abilities and resources of the client.

- consider the need for more support mechanisms:
  - increased frequency of contact
  - greater range of personnel in contact

- – accessing place of respite
- – intensive crisis intervention

- be aware of access to emergency procedures:
  - – cognitive approaches
  - explain the thoughts as symptoms
  - – explain the possibility of treating 'hopelessness'
  - help to find reasons for living
  - generate active solutions
  - – create distractions
  - – involve the extended network of supports

- have clear explanations of what can, and cannot, be expected of services:
  - – what responsibilities belong with the person, the carers, and the services (for example, all the possible interventions may not ultimately ensure that a person will live).

CASE EXAMPLE

Sheila telephones the CMHT to say she intends to take an overdose of 100 paracetamol tablets. She reminds you that she has a long history of serious suicide attempts, overdosing and wrist-cutting. She states that the mental health services have nothing left to offer her and she will be at peace when she finally summons up the courage to end it all.

You encourage Sheila to stay on the phone, to discuss what she is feeling at present and what has changed recently. You tell her that you accept what she feels, but that it sometimes takes someone else to help her to see the positive changes that have been and can be achieved.

You explain that it is important that Sheila remains informed of what is happening — telling her that you will visit (giving an exact time) and that you will inform significant others, such as her psychiatrist, GP, carer, A&E department, as appropriate and take note of her response to these suggestions. She is encouraged by you to remain involved in all discussions of options for support.

Sheila denies that any of these options will be of any use and states she will take the overdose before you can arrive. You inform Sheila of all the options that are within your control, but that she also has to accept her own responsibility for decisions and actions — you cannot ultimately be responsible for keeping her alive if she is intent on dismissing help and acting before anyone can be with her.

You accurately record the discussions, the immediate contacts with others and your plan of action to respond to the crisis.

Severe self-neglect

- encourage regular health promotion strategies, for example:
  - regular contact with the GP
  - advice on access to cheap, nutritious meals in the local area
  - realistic opportunities for relaxation and exercise
- practical strategies for problem solving, for example:
  - meals-on-wheels instead of cooking
  - budgeting advice
  - power keys for using electricity
- developing structure to the day, for example:
  - dividing time up between different daily living skills
  - activities
  - building plans around service user's expressed interests
  - negotiating visits by all people in the care and support network
- supporting carers and other domiciliary services, for example:
  - psycho-education
  - behavioural family therapy
- consider legal powers; for example, guardianship
- involve environmental health when necessary
- negotiate compromises on payments/repayments with providers of utility services (gas, electricity, water)
- ensure all benefits entitlements have been accessed
- consider supported accommodation

CASE EXAMPLE

Charlie is an elderly man living alone in a one-bedroom flat after several years as a resident of a long-stay hospital ward (he prefers his sense of independence). He is still hearing voices and is now experiencing shaky hands. He sits in his living-room chair for most of the day and night, every day. He is described as neglectful of himself by his family and neighbours, who feel that he should be back in the hospital where he would be looked after. Charlie accepts the support of a home help and makes himself a basic meal each day. He does not see the need to clean up or tidy the flat.

You encourage Charlie to focus his daily activity around a visit to local shops and the scheduled visit by the home help. He agrees to you accompanying him to the local shops, to explain his needs and ensure them he is being supported. They agree to contact you if he has any difficulties, either with his visits or from the local youths.

Continued overleaf...

CASE EXAMPLE/Continued:

As the CMHT key worker, you agree regular visits with Charlie, which will enable you to monitor his mental state, medication adherence and personal wishes. You also take a lead role in discussing and encouraging the family and neighbours to take a different view of Charlie's needs, even encouraging their active support. Charlie's daily living skills do not change, he does not see this as a problem and those living close to him agree to tolerate his situation as long as the services do not reduce their contacts.

■ **Which of the above strategies are you confident in and what do you need to prioritise for your own personal training?**

Personal skills

Debate and argument about the core competencies and skills of each mental health profession continue in many forums around the UK, including the Sainsbury Centre for Mental Health. Core competencies such as comprehensive assessment, individual care planning, service monitoring and review are relevant across all areas of mental health practice, for example:

- acute care and long-term rehabilitation
- primary and secondary care
- medical conditions characterised as psychoses and neuroses
- medical and psychosocial interventions.

The personal skills required may differ for specialist areas of service delivery; for example, the difficult to engage, or treatment resistant, client group. Clinical experiences and the wide-ranging literature on the services for people with severe and enduring mental health problems indicate the value of fundamental personal skills which do not belong to any one specific profession, or even necessarily to the profession-ally qualified. These can be seen to translate to all aspects of effective treatment, rehabilitation and support, including the function of risk management.

While many skills are a product of learning, through exposure to information and experience, attitudes may be developed through learning or may be innate personal qualities.

Attitudes and attributions

The challenges of severe and enduring mental health problems, including the occurrence of aggression and violence, suicidal ideas, self-harming behaviours and severe self-neglect require a set of values and attitudes that include:

- an accepting approach
- non-judgmental responses
- enquiring into causal relationships.

There is little to gain from:

- imposing personal standards without negotiation

- expectations of rapid change

- quickly attributing blame to the service user.

Some aspects of the work require a shift in attitude towards the responsibilities you are prepared to assume, particularly an openness to accept challenging working conditions that may not be within the bounds of the traditional organisation of services. Working where the service user feels more comfortable and in more creative ways with the conditions and environments within which they often exist, can challenge our earlier professional parameters. Taking a *longitudinal* view of expectations of change means working at the individual service users pace, with their priorities. Workers need to frequently seek very small changes as indications of achievement and change. These may not always correspond with the broad statement of goals and expectations that services demand of themselves (Patterson *et al.*, 1997).

In relation to risk and relapse of the medical condition, this longitudinal view may help to facilitate a worker's development of anticipation of future behaviour patterns and events, with benefits to the processes of prediction and management of such risks as violence or suicide attempts.

The approaches developed through intensive case management and assertive outreach acknowledge the need to get to know the individual. Patterson *et al.* state that such an approach, in relation to identifying risk behaviours (for example, violence or self-harming) enables us to understand what may act as a calming influence or a trigger to the individual emotional responses to different situations. A focus on short-term goals and brief interventions will not enable such work and can generally be attributed to the different sets of attitudes and expectations that effectively support other specialist areas of work; for example, anxiety management or short-term cognitive analytical therapy.

Flexibility

People are individuals and this requires a flexible response from those who are working with their treatment, support, and management of the risks. Consistency and firmness can have its place; for example, dealing with the need to set limits and boundaries with people deemed to be personality disordered. However, the limitless range of situations that may be encountered within mental health services requires a wide repertoire of practical responses, from the individual and the wider multidisciplinary team.

The assumption that a person placed onto the Supervision Register requires very close and intensive contact does not always follow. The focus is on multidisciplinary agreement as to the appropriate levels and types of supervision. Sometimes we need to take a more considered look at how we may best achieve monitoring, through indirect contacts such as letters, telephone calls, and collaborating with a broader network of support. The emphasis is on maintaining the agreed supervision; the assertive outreach approaches to service delivery will offer creative opportunities for achieving these aims.

Engagement

The basis for effective treatment and the minimisation of risk must start from a basis of developing a trusting working relationship. The methods for achieving this are as varied and individual as the people we encounter (Morgan, 1996). It does not always mean that our assessment of a problem is shared by the service user, particularly in instances of severe self-neglect with its characteristic features of service-user denial of the problems. Simple differences of opinion can lead to failed engagement, requiring more creative approaches to the individual circumstances; for example, engaging more closely with the informal carers to offer our advice and support.

Outward calmness

Whatever the feelings inside, when faced with a serious incident of risk, an outer portrayal of calmness instils confidence in others and offers an edge in the face of crisis. Seeing the incident within the longitudinal picture helps to contain your own sense of crisis. Demonstrating calm and slowed verbal and non-verbal responses helps to de-escalate the sense of crisis in others. Many people are surprised how the adrenaline rush brings about some of these automatic calming responses in a crisis, but there is always time to remind ourselves of them and even some rehearsal of how, ideally, we would like to respond in a crisis.

Accepting responsibility

Accepting responsibility means being aware of the responsibilities you are expected to carry (discussed further in **Chapter Five: Accountability and responsibility**), including the differentiation of clinical, operational and key worker responsibilities.

Positive risk taking

Not all management of risk should be about restriction and negative responses, though we do have to ensure that the damaging impacts of risk are minimised. Service users have the same rights to choice as anyone else (except in rare, exceptional circumstances). Positive risk-taking should be about encouraging people to take chances in an environment of support, monitoring and learning, which also seeks to minimise the impacts of the risks.

Maltsberger (1994) discusses the management of intractably suicidal people, outlining the notions of reasonable expectations; where clinicians will do all within their ability and power to prevent a successful suicide, but there are also circumstances in which responsibilities for actions may be explicitly spelled out and handed back to the client. Alternative options need to be weighed up in the light of individual circumstances. This should be a multidisciplinary activity, but by the very nature of suicidal behaviours, it may present as a dilemma to an individual clinician to manage in crisis:

- do I attempt to take control, in order to save this person?
- what can realistically be done and not be done in specific circumstances?
- being open to the service user about your limitations and what responsibilities they ultimately carry for their own decisions and actions, that is, the things it would be impossible for you to do to prevent a fatal outcome

- acknowledging explicitly that sometimes the notion of restriction and containment may not achieve the desired effect — patients do kill themselves on hospital wards and in other secure environments.

A duty of care includes:

- performing professional responsibilities to an accepted standard
- considering all the options with relevant others, where permissible by time and accessibility
- clearly documenting discussions, decisions and interventions
- being explicit about what is possible and what is clearly impossible in the light of:
  - time
  - place
  - resources available
  - expectations.

Empowering

Successful risk prevention and management stems from involving the service user and carer in all stages of the process of:

- discussion
- choices
- priorities
- negotiations
- decisions
- treatment, rehabilitation and supportive interventions.

This is not about undermining professional judgement, but it does require a different conceptual framework to that instilled in the training of most health professionals; which will include an understanding that:

- risk is not always about restriction
- action is not always about taking over
- service responses are not always about assessment under the Mental Health Act.

However, sometimes it will be about these approaches, as a last resort, to minimise the impact of a serious incident on the service user and/or others. Education and information-sharing are two essential ingredients to this skill.

Negotiation

The individuality of the person, combined with the complexity of their needs/circumstances, frequently involves a minefield of conflicts and viewpoints. An essential skill is that of identifying:

- who are the key players in the CPA process?
- what is the extent of the knowledge and limits of understanding of the issues of mental health and social care in the individual circumstances of the case?

- what is the scope for compromise between the different interests in this group of people?

- whose views should take precedence, in which circumstances?

This process is entirely dependent on your communicating directly and indirectly with all the participants, which will involve you in any combination of negotiations with the service user, carer(s) and a range of other workers/agencies. Success requires patience and the ability to separate out a staged approach to the range of discussions; that is, it may take several individual meetings, back and forth between the different people involved. You should be mindful not to lose the important views of the service user in this process.

Time management

Appropriate use or priority on time can help prevent some risks increasing to the danger level. However, successful risk management requires time, not just to meet with the service user, but for the whole process of communicating and co-ordinating a network of support.

Confidentiality

Appropriate use of this element enables engagement of a trusting relationship and failure to comply can bring about a rapid deterioration. A good relationship can be used in times of reduced risk, to explore the value of sharing information with those who need to know, in the interests of continued good risk management. However, there will be very rare occasions when confidentiality may need to be breached, when a serious incident of risk is imminent (Department of Health, 1996). These occasions will most likely be characterised by:

- the development of a recognised previous pattern, or identification of a new pattern of serious risk behaviour (likely to cause serious danger to self or others)

- known likely victims of the risk behaviour

- no change to the development of the pattern anticipated from discussion with the service user themselves, or a complete rejection of others

- the need to inform those at immediate risk, so that action can be taken to prevent or minimise the dangerous consequences.

Confidentiality tends to be more of an issue when the 'need to know', and to whom it applies, have not been openly discussed with the service user. If the issue is left open to individual interpretation, then the most fearful perceptions that *everyone* has a right to know your mental health and risk history may prevail. In these instances, agreements on confidentiality may be less forthcoming.

The practice of more open engagement, promoted through assertive outreach and a range of effective treatments and supports, is the most likely way of establishing the trust required for agreeing the limits of confidentiality. As a guide, those involved in the CPA multidisciplinary team would be the people with a claim to a 'need to know'.

Continuing learning

The rapidly changing demands on services and the complexity of the whole issue of risk requires that practitioners are open to regular training and new learning. The very nature of many of the skills outlined above demands a flexibility in approach, in order that we may achieve better risk management and consequent risk minimisation. The growing recognition of the need for multidisciplinary training is one area that is enhancing our knowledge, skills and abilities across the range of demands that risk presents (Duggan, 1997b).

Recording risk management plans

The recording of a risk management plan will be one element of a much broader care plan that will cover the primary functions of effective treatment, rehabilitation and support. In reality, the risk management plan will concentrate on the focused issues that may initiate or escalate a crisis or relapse with potential dangers to self or others.

Within the procedural requirements of the locally implemented guidance and legislation, we need a format that will offer a combination of the immediate responses to situations and the longer-term development of the risk management plan. The format outlined in the **Trainer's manual** accompanying this handbook is designed with these requirements in mind. The sections cover:

1 Registration within the broad context of the local CPA and sub-registers of specialist risk categories.

2 The client/carer in the process is helped to understand and make sense of the procedural requirements; for example:
  - the key worker meeting with them to explain and prepare service users and carers for the main meeting
  - flexibility organised to encourage, not discourage, participation; for example, this may involve sub-dividing into separate smaller meetings rather than one large over-bearing meeting
  - their wishes being elicited, recorded and recognised within the discussion and the decision process
  - resolution/negotiation of differences (for example, meeting service user and carer separately, to discuss the different options or taking the lead where differences prevail)
  - active involvement in the decisions (for example, counter-signing care plans).

3 Others involved in the management plan:
  - identifying the need to see risk management as an exercise in co-operation between individuals and agencies
  - identifying the relevant key worker(s) with responsibility for overseeing the co-ordination of the plan and effective communication takes place.

4 Specifically identified risks:
  - clearly communicating the risks to all relevant people in terms of:
    - categories; for example, violence, self-harm or self-neglect
    - behaviours and/or cognitions specific to the individual's own experience of risk
    - situational context of factors the individual responds to
    - systems; the context in which services are organised and are expected to function

- issues of confidentiality need to be addressed, but risk issues require that all people who could be potential victims, or affected by incidents of violence, suicide or neglect, have a right to know and to try to manage such potential situations.

5 Interventions for the above information:
- identifying who will be doing what, when and how
- flexibility is essential, but shared and agreed guidelines and strategies will aid everyone to be clearer in their observations and actions.

6 Strengths and opportunities to support the plan:
- identifying the resources that all involved people can offer, particularly from service users and carers.

7 Dangers or difficulties hindering the plan:
- sharing information from combined assessments of what problems may impede the successful implementation of agreed plans.

8 Crisis response procedures:
- sharing knowledge of what crisis or emergency procedures are available in the local area
- estimating what form a crisis or emergency may take for an individual while acknowledging that we may not be completely accurate in these predictions
- outlining who may be responsible for doing what, when and how in such circumstances.

9 Noting the frequency of reviews of the plan, with time, date and place for next meeting recorded:
- the key worker will be responsible for co-ordinating this next meeting, or for calling a sooner meeting if a crisis or failure of the plan requires
- the signature of the key worker(s) should represent collective responsibility for the plan; but you may wish to develop a format that names all people involved, not only the key worker(s).

The risk management plan should be practical and specific. Elaboration of the discussions about management options will offer some degree of protection, if the need for scrutiny and inquiry unfortunately arose. However, these will need to be clearly documented in the context of care planning for the individual service user.

> ■ **How may this type of format fit with the local service agreement on documenting care plans?**

Staff training issues

1 Co-ordination of multidisciplinary meetings and care plans, including risk management plans as a sub-category (sometimes the prominent issues).

2 Flexible approaches to engagement that reflect individual service user needs and wishes.

3 Analysis of the national and local context of the CPA, Supervision Register and Supervised Discharge implementation.

4 Accountability and responsibility at individual, team and organisation levels.

5 Clarifying clinical, managerial and consultative roles of different staff in relation to risk management issues and the delivery of effective treatment, rehabilitation and supportive interventions.

6 Clinical risk management techniques and interventions, for use before, during and after an incident of risk, such as violence, suicide or neglect.

7 Negotiating skills for resolving the conflicting demands of service users, carers, and diverse agencies.

8 Preparation for appearing before, and reporting to, panels of inquiry, serious incidents committees, or the coroner's court.

Some of the above issues in relation to the system risks will be considered in the next two chapters.

■ **What do you identify as the current risk management training needs at the individual and team levels in your local service?**

CHAPTER

 **FOUR** SERVICE ORGANISATION

Introduction

This chapter aims to help professional and non-professional service providers to appreciate:

- that the way teams and services are organised can influence their effectiveness and their ability to offer comprehensive and safe services

- the need for developing clear service priorities, in order to guide the allocation of the finite resources between the relatively infinite demands

- the difficulties posed to practitioners by the way the broad mental health system is divided across different sectors; that is, more dispersed services present a greater challenge for effective communication and co-ordination.

The effective assessment and management of risk requires the combined involvement and expertise of many people, frequently working within different agencies, organisations and professions. The same can be said for the delivery of effective treatment and support provided by comprehensive services to meet the complex needs of service users. The communication between and co-ordination of a diverse range of individuals is the key to identifying and minimising the incidence of:

- aggression and violence

- suicide and self-harm

- severe self-neglect

- service user exploitation

- others

However, these people frequently function in very different ways, with different:

- operational policies

- professional codes

- service philosophies

- personal attitudes

- procedural arrangements

- priorities and resources.

Thus, we have the ingredients for systems risk whereby the very nature of the working methods and practices contribute to the potential likelihood of the risks they attempt to avoid.

Harrison (1997) refers to the dangers of using bureaucratic procedures as a form of defensive practice, with the outcome being that more time is diverted into form-filling, and less into therapeutic activity. He suggests that examples of poor practice have justified the introduction of successive pieces of guidance and legislation, but *'the institutional walls of the old hospitals are simply replaced by institutional walls of paperwork'*.

Highlighting service failings

Sheppard (1996) details the findings and recommendations of several reports of inquiry into tragic events involving users of mental health services. It provides a salutary reminder to all service providers, managers and clinicians that things do go wrong, but with alarming similarities that suggest the lessons are not being learned. While expectations need to be reasonable about what can be achieved, working in the context of human emotions and behaviours, we should not become complacent to the very real dangers that repeated poor practice can present.

The Ritchie Report (Ritchie *et al.*, 1994) into the care and treatment of Christopher Clunis provides a comprehensive account of an investigation into a catalogue of missed opportunities and failed procedures at individual and service levels. As a result of ten reported assaults (four of a serious nature) frequently including knives, the police and the criminal justice system were regularly involved. Christopher Clunis also had frequent contact with mental health and homeless agencies.

Lambeth, Southwark and Lewisham Health Commission (1994) summarised the involvement of services between 1986 and 1992 as follows:

- eight hospitals
- thirteen consultant psychiatrists
- five GPs
- five community psychiatric nurses
- four social workers
- five housing departments
- four hostels
- one occupational therapist
- four bed-and-breakfast placements.

Ritchie *et al.*, instead of condemning one specific individual, service or agency, set out to document a cumulative pattern of failure and missed opportunities. The overriding failure is that of inadequate communication, liaison and transfer of information between the numerous agencies involved. The result is the inadequate delivery of treatment and support to an individual in need, with far-reaching tragic consequences. At a service organisation level, the findings include:

- poor liaison between individuals from different agencies

- a lack of managed co-ordination between health and social services

- section 117 after-care procedures not closely implemented

- poor liaison across geographical boundaries, as well as across service sectors

- a failure to adopt assertive outreach, or to address early warning signs of relapse

- a failure to obtain a full, accurate and verified history

- a failure to involve the original GP.

At a clinical level, several deficiencies are reported:

- failure to verify an accurate history was compounded by an over-reliance on Christopher Clunis' own deluded accounts

- a lack of awareness of the location and contacts with family members

- repeated consideration of Christopher Clunis as an 'itinerant homeless person'

- a failure to chart the relationship of offending behaviours to mental disorder, frequently resulting in misleading predictions and false reassurances about his potential for dangerous behaviour

- a neglect of the rule that the best predictor of future behaviour is past behaviour.

One implication is that guidance from an organisational level about clearly focused risk decision-making processes may help to address the above issues and any others that may be deemed significant to a specific set of circumstances.

Decision-making processes

The way we come to particular decisions is rarely afforded any detailed analysis within mental health teams. It may be that the process is ultimately influenced by specific personalities, or frequently by the influence of the medical profession. Good decisions must be informed by detailed discussion of complex issues in a multidisciplinary forum. Consideration of how decisions are made will be of value to:

- individual practitioners

- multidisciplinary teams

- the service/organisation.

Consideration should be given to how we make decisions, for example:

- individual vs. collective

- intuition vs. weighing pros and cons

- user needs vs. service needs

- others

There is no right or wrong way, as the variety of circumstances will influence the methods used at any given time. Ideally, we should aim for decision making that is collective, user-centred, and carefully considered. However, the example of a crisis will not necessarily permit such contemplation; it will demand that a more instant and rapid response is made. Being aware of the different influences on a given decision can be as valuable as the decision itself — certainly for gaining support from others, if it has to be justified under scrutiny, following an incident of any kind.

What information do we need? This will depend on your judgement of:

- who is involved?
- what are the expected aims and outcomes?
- how quickly does the decision need to be made?
- what risks may be involved?
- are there issues of confidentiality?
- where are the sources of information?
- how quickly can they be accessed?

How may you access the main sources of information:

- do you need special permission?
- do you need a high authority, for example, senior management or clinical director?
- are there any inter-agency agreements or differences on confidentiality?
- is it a simple phone call or visit, or does it require the lengthy process of a written request?
- what happens if you fail to access the information?
- what happens if you document your attempts and requests?

Who is involved in processing the information into a practical decision?

■ **Can you identify the different types of decision-making processes that are used, individually and collectively, within your team or service?**

Decision-making traps

Carson (1994) suggests that the process of assessing the level of risk in any given set of circumstances is fraught with difficulties. The multidisciplinary team needs to be aware of the possibilities for error. Some of the more significant pitfalls are summarised as:

- plunging in; reaching conclusions on insufficient information or thought
- off track; setting about the wrong problem, following a focus on the wrong mental framework or attitudes
- external influence; giving priority to the views of others when defining the problem
- over-confidence; allowing your opinions and judgements to obscure key information
- short cuts; using generalisations or convenient information inappropriately
- shooting from the hip; failure to balance intuition with systematic procedure
- group failure; failure to manage good ideas towards practical decisions

- blind spots; incorrectly interpreting the evidence from past history and experience

- not keeping track; failure to accurately record the details of past events and sequences.

> ■ **Can you identify practical examples of how each of the above may occur in your team or service?**

Systematic processes and procedures within a team or service may help to avoid some of these traps. However, any system that deals with the intricacies of human behaviour will always need to be tempered by a degree of flexibility to accommodate intuition and individual circumstances.

Why may our procedures fail?

Tyrer & Kennedy (1995) suggest that *'the [Supervision] Register, if properly used, is a powerful tool for negotiating the proper level of investment by identifying the number, needs, gaps in provision and risks to the community'*. If we did not have the current procedural arrangements, we would have to invent something almost identical.

The procedural arrangements of the CPA, Supervision Register and Supervised Discharge have been outlined in **Chapter Three: Risk management**, but the implication of media representation and clinical anecdote would suggest that all is not as efficient as Tyrer & Kennedy suggest.

McCarthy *et al.* (1995) state that *'Although the principles behind the introduction of the care programme approach have been welcomed, in practice, its implementation has at best been patchy, and at worst an almost complete failure'*.

The reasons behind these responses include:

- inclusion criteria are too broad

- an emphasis on the bureaucratic functions of administration and paperwork is likely to draw attention away from direct clinical contacts, particularly when no additional resources are forthcoming

- roles and responsibilities within the changing patterns of service delivery have rarely been adequately clarified in the multidisciplinary teams

- targeting resources has not been as clear in practice as it seems to be in theory

- little acknowledgement has been made of the time resource required for clinicians to be effective communicators and co-ordinators

(Caldicott, 1994; Holloway, 1994; Vaughan, 1998).

At a more practical level, the exercise on implementing the CPA which is included in the accompanying **Trainer's manual** has been widely tested in workshop conditions with clinicians, managers and non-professionals. Of the many discussions that result, there appears to be a consensus on why the CPA so frequently fails in practice:

- over-burdened staff, with inadequate time to prepare for meetings

- no prior agenda to guide the meeting

- poor consistency of attendance, sometimes including people who have not necessarily met the service user
- excluding key players, for example GPs, by poor timing and location of meetings
- no clear definitions of responsibilities; for example:
  - for key worker role
  - who is chairing the meeting
  - who takes the minutes
  - how to implement collective decision making
- occasionally organised to fit the consultant psychiatrist's timetable
- inadequate time set aside to adequately fulfil the functions, particularly in the more complex cases
- busy staff/services with their own agendas for avoiding taking on more work
- hierarchical service approach, that diminishes or excludes the views of many people who hold the most significant information regarding current and historical risks, for example:
  - service users
  - carers
  - support workers
  - voluntary sector workers
- inadequate, or poorly targeted, training about the local implementation of the guidance
- fear of the repercussions of identifying unmet needs, that is, you will have to stretch further to meet it
- a lack of practical local guidelines spelling out the needs and resources for good practice in implementation.

> ■ **Critically analyse the reasons why you felt that CPA in which you have been involved have been good and/or bad experiences.**

Organisational requirements

- clinical systems (for example, CPA/care management) which will effectively 'trigger' risk issues, for discussion and for risk management decisions
- clear targeting, with sufficient resources and reasonable caseloads
- staff who are well trained and understand the concepts of assessment and management of risk and how they inter-relate
- staff who understand the concepts of accountability and responsibility (see **Chapter Five**) and are supported by senior management in their application
- relevant inter-agency agreements (statutory and non-statutory bodies) to ensure high quality communication and co-ordination across services

Resources

This should not simply be seen as a numbers game, it involves careful consideration of service priorities, facilities, support and training. Good practice for effective treatment, rehabilitation and support requires adequate resources, which in turn will minimise the need for risk management responses. This good practice could include:

- a specialist focus, through clear priorities for targeting
- adequate staffing of specialist assertive outreach teams (caseloads of 12–15)
- assertive outreach to the community and inreach to in-patient units at times of hospital admission
- specialist teams to be an integral part of a comprehensive range of mental health services
- seven-day availability, with 24-hour crisis response
- availability of in-patient beds, to which the community team could gate-keep the admission
- access to secure environments, if needed
- access to highly supervised accommodation in the community, to avoid hospital admission, whenever possible
- regular training and support
- service user consultation on their needs of specialist services.

The costs of such a service needs to be evaluated beside the costs of less intensive support leading to less co-ordinated use of expensive hospital beds. The economic equation is not simple. This is not a service blueprint for all types of provision; it needs to be carefully targeted and to recruit those staff who have the abilities and attitudes to develop this style of working outlined (not all staff will want to work solely with the client groups experiencing severe and enduring mental health problems).

■ **Do you feel these functions require specialist teams, specialists within teams, or the responsibilities to be accepted by all staff?**

■ **What types of supervision and support will be required in your decisions on the above question?**

Clarity of roles

Service configuration has gone through a number of contortions in different localities, with many staff feeling as if they inhabit a 'merry-go-round'. Community-orientated, multidisciplinary, integrated service provision is generally accepted. How the responsibilities in professional and managerial roles change, to meet the new structures, is less clear.

Essential requirements that need addressing include:

- professional vs. operational management — separating out the clinical and the day-to-day team-functioning responsibilities
- team leader vs. consultant psychiatrist responsibilities — determining the managerial authority for setting the team priorities and targets

- leadership functions and styles; for example:
  - involvement in decision making
  - resolving conflicts
  - encouraging commitment
- professional vs. line-management supervision structures within and without the team.

Communication

Professionals have a duty to balance confidentiality with the need to know, particularly regarding colleagues from other agencies; for example, housing, probation, voluntary sector (Reed, 1997). This specifically applies to information which may be contained in risk management plans.

The issue of confidentiality is further clouded by the duty of care you hold to others, to pass on information to a third party you know to be at risk (Department of Health, 1996). This was particularly highlighted by the case in the US of Tarasoff vs. Regents of the University of California (Turner & Kennedy, 1997).

Failure to communicate key information is one of the most important problems highlighted by successive reports of inquiry. Appeals to confidentiality will not be accepted as an excuse for poor or inaccurate communication. It is a duty on local organisations to develop agreements about confidentiality and the need to share information, particularly where incidents of serious risk are the likely outcomes. (Department of Health, 1996).

A role for clinical audit?

Crombie *et al.* (1993) define audit as *'the process of reviewing the delivery of healthcare to identify deficiencies so that they may be remedied'*. A definition that may feed into the clinicians' more negative perceptions of management, checking up with a view to finding fault in their practice. Indeed, audit is frequently seen by clinicians as a bi-product of internal markets and management processes, with little direct relevance to the activity of busy clinicians.

Ovretveit (1992) outlines a broader definition, identifying quality in the clinical, professional and managerial dimensions. Thus, opening up the possibilities that it can be relevant to the service practitioners and even identify issues of user satisfaction with clearly defined areas of service delivery.

Ash (1997) outlines a method of developing audit as a clinically relevant multidisciplinary tool for reviewing aspects of care and support, looking at structure, process, outcome, and user satisfaction.

In relation to the areas of assessment and management of risk, the fear is that audit will primarily serve to underpin criticisms of already burdened clinical services. If the functions are clearly spelt out to the local service, these fears need not materialise.

Clinical audit departments should be able to offer the following support to clinical services:

- reports on levels of risk activity across the service
- statistical information to support targeting decisions
- half-day presentations on relevant issues, using case study approaches to highlight examples of good practice

- organise speakers to present relevant information
- a focus for identifying user views and satisfaction
- a researched base to decisions on training priorities.

The challenge is to gather and present clinically relevant information that will shape decisions, without involving busy clinicians in additional activity that could be viewed as managerial-oriented and viewed with degrees of suspicion.

> ■ **Can you identify the people involved in clinical audit in your organisation and what information they have provided for clinical services?**

CHAPTER FIVE

ACCOUNTABILITY AND RESPONSIBILITY

Introduction

A strongly held assumption by many service practitioners is a concern that they will be individually scapegoated when a treatment decision goes wrong, particularly if an incident of some kind results. The requirements of the CPA, Supervision Register and Supervised Discharge, to have named key workers/supervisors, is upheld as the evidence that will be used for allocating blame when incidents occur.

Tyrer & Kennedy (1995) have attempted to challenge this assumption, stating that correct use of the guidance will be accompanied by a distribution of responsibilities, shared between individual, team, managers, and employers. They also highlight that some decisions involving issues of risk will inevitably go wrong. We cannot achieve risk *elimination*, but we can expect that all efforts are made to achieve risk *minimisation*.

If we are to shift from a negative culture of blame to a more positive culture characterised by encouragement and support, these responsibilities need to be clearly apportioned across the levels referred to above and risk decisions will need to be informed by identifiable policy guidelines.

Divisions of responsibility

Carson (1995) states that individual practitioners will be responsible for the day-to-day decisions they make in relation to their professional practice. Good quality decisions should be promoted by the plans agreed by the multidisciplinary team. These plans will, in turn, be informed by the policy guidelines agreed and disseminated by the senior managers and employers in the organisation. Carson (1995) reminds us, even with the best quality decisions, harm will still occasionally result. The decisions can be justified by their relationship to the agreed procedures developed within the organisation.

Senior managers of the trust or authority have a responsibility to develop a policy for risk decisions that promotes encouragement and support for the service practitioners and multidisciplinary teams. Reed (1997) suggests that it is unreasonable to criticise practitioners who have made every effort to implement recognised good practice, but, despite these efforts, something still goes tragically wrong. If an incident results in treatment decisions being scrutinised in a court of law or an inquiry, shared accountability for reasonable decisions can be assumed if the link can be demonstrated between: the individual decision/team plan/organisational policy/government guidelines.

The nature of accountability

- each individual is accountable for their actions within the sphere of their professional competence

- individual accountability cannot be devolved to, or assumed by, others. Training and qualification attaches certain reasonable expectations of clinical competence to practising professionals

- you cannot be held accountable for factors over which you had no control and for information you could not access. But, you must be able to demonstrate *reasonable* attempts to gain relevant information

- terms such as *clinical* or *overall* accountability become confusing. We need to more clearly state what we expect of team leader, key worker, and clinical profession accountability, as they contribute towards the shared decisions made by a group of people

- it is vitally important that individuals and groups of decision-makers, carefully think through the process of arriving at plans of action. Snowden (1997) suggests the need for routine self-questioning, along the lines of:

    - do I know what the risks are (in the clinical and/or social context)?

    - do I have the necessary information on which to base treatment decisions and plans?

    - am I cutting corners or trying to save time?

    - do we need to take this risk now, to enhance treatment and progress?

    - what might be achieved, or what might happen if we act or do not act?

    - how do I justify this action: to myself, colleagues, service users and carers?

    - are there any discrepancies in the thinking behind the decision?

    - is the decision rational, in relation to the available information?

    - is there a rigorous formulation of the case, based on a full multidisciplinary assessment of the available information?

This process should not be about supporting defensive practice. Carson (1996) suggests that *'risk taking involves the most exciting, the most intellectual and professional parts of the job, although also the most anxiety-provoking parts'*. He goes on to argue in favour of a direction where *'simplistic, defensive, cover-our-backs attitudes to risk taking may lead to liability'*.

Dilemmas and expectations

Prins (1990) states *'one of the most crucial dilemmas faced by those involved in decisions concerning the detention or discharge of persons who have exhibited, or are thought likely to exhibit, dangerous behaviour is the need for them to balance the need to act in the interests of the community as agents of control and custody on the one hand and to serve the interests of the individual on the other'*.

In coming to these decisions, we require a certain degree of acceptance that what we are frequently dealing with is human emotions, sometimes at their more distressed, volatile and bizarre. We are thus being confronted with a requirement to predict what seems quite unpredictable, by its very nature. This difficulty with prediction means that our focus must be on risk minimisation or harm reduction, through the effective application of the skills of assessment, treatment and support.

It is reasonable, however, to expect that practitioners will:

- work to recognised professional standards

- access all available information

- make thorough assessments on the available information

- demonstrate informed risk decision-making processes

- make reasoned and justifiable decisions

- access relevant training for the tasks at hand.

Levels of responsibility

Individual practitioner

The following recommendations closely resemble the role of the key worker stated in the CPA (Department of Health, 1995). They apply primarily to effective treatment and support, but also to the specific focus on the complex issues of risk:

1 Close monitoring of the service user, including:
- agreed therapeutic interventions
- indirect contacts with social supports
- eliciting the service user's views on care and treatment.

2 Co-ordination of:
- the multidisciplinary team
- the broader network of support.

3 Calling and preparing care planning reviews (regular and extraordinary meetings):
- in-patient care planning:
  - ward key worker (link nurse) to arrange pre-discharge assessment and planning meeting
- community care co-ordinator/key worker (if already in place) to collaborate with in-patient team to ensure suitability of the environment and social circumstances for discharge
- community care planning:
  - meeting to be organised by person doing the initial assessment, or by the existing care co-ordinator/key worker
  - above person responsibility for ensuring the care plan is recorded.

4 Monitoring progress of the agreed plan:
- own input
- checking the progress of others.

5 Contribute relevant abilities to:

- accessing and sharing information
- continuous and thorough assessment
- identifying early warning signs of relapse/risks
- collective decision making on available information.

Multidisciplinary teams

1 Nominate and agree a key worker (must be present and agreeing to take the role).

2 Determine the key worker by relevant knowledge, skills and relationship factors, not simply by profession.

3 Agree the care plan (including a detailed risk management plan).

4 Agree subsequent changes to the plan.

5 Demonstrate good practice in:

- accessing and sharing information
- continuous and thorough assessment
- identifying early warning signs of relapse/risks
- collective decision making on available information.

Organisation

1 Communicate a corporate conceptualisation of risk, including:

- ideas on positive risk taking
- accessibility of information
- issues of confidentiality
- service user consultation and involvement.

2 Develop risk policy guidelines, including:

- incorporation of the above conceptualisation
- risk assessment
- risk management (including the implementation of national guidance)
- risk decision making
- inter-agency mechanisms/agreements.

3 Explicit mechanisms of support and supervision, including:

- levels of accountability and responsibility
- pressing charges, when appropriate

- access to legal advice, in above circumstances

- access to specialist clinical supervision; for example, from forensic specialists

- equal opportunities for support extended to service users

- access and develop opportunities for regular and relevant training

- develop a proactive use of clinical audit.

4 Establish serious incidents procedures to:

- define risks and/or serious incidents

- investigate serious incidents

- change policy in the light of findings

- disseminate information to all relevant people.

The **Trainer's manual** which accompanies this handbook outlines how to develop guidelines for a risk policy (see **Session 8**), reflecting much of the information across the above levels of responsibility.

- ■ **What policies are you aware of, within your own organisation, that guide individuals and teams in their responsibilities to work with risk?**

- ■ **What gaps can you identify in your organisational policy, that you feel need attention (use the following service audit to guide your thinking)?**

Service audit of risk procedures and policies

1 Does your organisation have a specific policy on risk and/or personal safety?

2 Within this policy, do you have clear statements on the support and supervision to be offered to staff:

- working with high risk users of services

- when incidents occur?

3 How are these policy statements disseminated to the most junior staff in your organisation?

4 Does your organisation have an active definition of risk?

5 What procedures do you have in place to ensure service user involvement in the discussion of risk issues at the levels of:

- individual working relationships

- policy consultation?

6 Does your organisation offer and/or provide optional or mandatory training for staff on issues of risk assessment and management?

7 If you have training events, are service users involved in delivery and/or discussion of the material?

8 How are high risk referrals allocated within your service?

9 What system exists for prioritising high risk individuals within the total caseload of your service?

10 Do you have a system of documenting and filing risk, that is easily identifiable to all relevant people in your service?

11 Do you have a policy statement on confidentiality in relation to issues of risk?

12 How do you review your systems related to issues of risk, both within teams, and at an inter-agency level?

Inquiries and courts

One of the greatest fears faced by most clinicians still remains unaddressed in any form of training and preparation — appearance before a:

- serious incidents committee
- coroner's court
- panel of inquiry.

Yet, if we accept that risk minimisation involves incidents still occurring, however diligent our plans and practices, then the fears will continue to become reality for some people. Serious incidents of an unpredictable nature do not select the workers, so it remains fairly arbitrary as to who will have to go through the process.

Public inquiries

Bennett (1996) summarises the trends in homicides committed by people with mental health problems. He states that the facts do not support any of the public perceptions about community care contributing to a worsening level of violence. However, since 1991, there has been a radical shift in the focus of the public inquiry to the investigation of homicides committed by discharged patients. While these inquiries have contributed valuable insights into the occasional unpredictability of behaviour and the occasional failures of service provision, they contribute greatly to the scapegoating and stigmatisation of people experiencing mental health problems. The vast majority of service users do not deserve the labels they subsequently receive, or the increasingly defensive practice of practitioners who also fear scapegoating (Bennett, 1996).

Muijen (1997a; 1997b) argues that the volume of inquiries and the powerful messages associated with them, has resulted in misleading conclusions. While many of the findings are similar, some have seemed contradictory and they are providing less direction for policy and practice as more and more reports are published. He argues that *'much would be gained by a more focused and deeper investigation of fewer incidents'*.

Assessing and Managing Risk

As the number of incidents is not on the increase, they offer little statistical evidence to support the representation of community care commonly found in the media. Therefore, they may be reasonably supplemented by an independent ombudsman to act on behalf of complainants and determine in what circumstances an inquiry may prove beneficial (Muijen, 1997a).

Inquiries should primarily be established to investigate:

- individual personal suffering
- local service failures
- issues of national policy.

There may be overlap of these in any one particular inquiry. The desired outcome should be to bring about positive service development and/or constructive policy change.

For individuals who have to appear before an inquiry, training should address adequate preparation, through understanding the:

- specific purpose and remit of the inquiry
- individual and collective lines of investigation
- ways in which clinical notes will be used
- means of disseminating the findings
- individual fears and needs for support.

Courts

A primary fear of practitioners in a climate of increasing litigation is that they will be the subject of claims for negligence. Harrison (1997) reminds us that the courts apply tests to determine reasonable standards, which ultimately hinge on whether or not you have followed guidelines of good practice that would be accepted by a 'responsible body of people' — your professional peers.

Duty of care is considered to include:

- adequate knowledge of conditions and their treatment
- due care in the application of that knowledge in the interests of the patient.

Carson (1996) suggests that *'Basically, we all owe duties of care to those whom we can, being reasonable about it, foresee we might damage by an act or an omission'*. However, in a climate where we are led to believe that community care confers upon us the safeguarding of the general public, he reminds us that there are limits to this duty of care.

In the event of a serious incident, the test of negligence is a complex one to prove, relying on:

- scrutiny of the individual circumstances
- a determination of your role and responsibilities
- the relationship to accepted standards of care
- a determination that harm has been caused in a foreseeable way.

Adherence to guidelines of good practice and accepted standards of care are good defences against claims of negligence.

> ■ **How may you pursue training within your service for the legal implications of your work?**

APPENDIX 1

QUESTIONING SOMEONE ABOUT THEIR RISK POTENTIAL

Introduction

Generally speaking, we should not separate out the questions relating to risk from the questions and style of interviewing, pertinent to a thorough assessment of complex needs and mental health issues. Remember, effective treatment and support based on a comprehensive assessment is the first line of service delivery and will, in itself, enable prevention of a great many risk situations developing to the point of causing concern.

However, issues of risk (particularly violence or suicide) pose concerns for many practitioners, particularly in relation to methods of eliciting the relevant information directly from the service user. For this reason, they will be dealt with separately from the more usual line of enquiry, in assessment interviews or the ongoing discussions in clinical interactions. Two main concerns are:

- if I question a service user directly about their risk history and intentions, will I simply be providing the trigger for the behaviours to occur?
- how do I approach the tasks of questioning about risk history and intentions?

While there may be rare instances when the line of inquiry is sufficient to trigger an act of violence against self or others, this is usually not the case. Service users usually prefer to be involved in the process of assessment and management, rather than being excluded by a practitioner who is hoping that 'if I don't ask the question, the risk will stay away'. Asking the questions is a valid way of demonstrating to a service user that:

- they will be listened to
- their views will be understood, and acted upon
- they are not the only person who is going through a particular experience
- they are involved in their treatment and care.

For the practitioner, asking the questions may:

- open an opportunity to explore different perceptions and opinions
- add important information to the assessment
- indicate repetition of worrying patterns of thoughts and/or behaviours
- offer a sense of real participation within a therapeutic process.

It should not be a matter of whether you should or should not ask the questions. Asking is, more often than not, more accurate than guessing. The issue is more accurately one of *how* to go about your line of inquiry.

There is no simple set of concrete directives, as each individual and situation requires a response tailored to the particular circumstances. However, your first judgements will be an initial assessment of presentation through non-verbal cues, which will influence your line of questioning. Further consideration will be given to:

- posture
- relative positioning
- degree of eye contact
- tone of voice
- use of language
- non-judgmental attitude.

One of the skills lies in the timing and balance of the questions. The most sensitive method would be to use short questions, few questions, and open questions (Morgan, 1996). Too many, or ill thought-out questions could be seen as a defence by the practitioner in an uncomfortable situation, or may lead the service user away from the matters that are most significant for them at the time (Nelson-Jones, 1988).

Suicide and violence will be separated out, to give a general guide to the types of questions you may need to use occasionally.

Think of ways that you and your colleagues may be able to use the questions below in practice sessions to help your confidence. You may also come up with your own different lists of questions.

Suicide and self-harm

Do not say: *'Hello, I'm Steve, your case manager. Are you thinking of killing yourself then?'*.

As a guide, you may wish to consider: *'Hello, I'm Steve, your case manager. You seem to be experiencing some kind of distress at present; how does this make you feel?'*. Supplementary questions will take their lead from the responses you receive.

Salford NHS Trust and Salford Social Services offer the following examples from their Adult Acute Services – Risk Assessment Tool:

Self-harm:

1 Have you harmed yourself at any time?

2 Describe what happened when you tried to harm yourself now or in the past?

3 Did you make a plan to harm yourself? Can you describe your plan?

4 Did you make any attempt to avoid discovery? If yes, how?

5 What were your reasons for the attempt?

6 What did you expect to be the outcome of your attempt?

7 How do you feel about what you did now?

8 Do you have a history of using alcohol or drugs?

Thoughts of self-harm:

1 Have you ever had thoughts of self-harm?

2 Can you describe these thoughts?

3 Do you have these thoughts now?

4 When was the last time you had these thoughts?

5 How long have you been thinking in this way and how often do these thoughts occur?

6 Prior to this, have you ever expressed these thoughts to anybody? If yes, who?

7 What was happening in your life when these thoughts started?

8 Are you thinking of a particular plan?

9 What is preventing/has prevented you from acting on these thoughts?

10 What would you do if these thoughts reoccurred?

11 How do you feel now?

These questions are only meant to act as a guide to your own approach.

Violence

Do not say: *'Hello I'm Steve, your case manager. I've looked at your medical notes, and you seem to be one dangerous so-and-so. Are you thinking of having a go at anyone again these days?'*.

As a guide, you may wish to consider: *'Hello, I'm Steve, your case manager. I've been checking through your medical notes recently, and there seem to be situations that have angered you in the past. Can you tell me what it was that caused you to feel this way?'*.

Salford NHS Trust and Salford Social Services offer the following examples from their Adult Acute Services – Risk Assessment Tool:

Potential harm to others:

1 Have you ever, now or in the past, had thoughts or acted on thoughts about harming others?

2 How often do you think about harming others?

3 What has prevented you from acting on your thoughts?

4 Have you ever been in trouble with the police?

5 If you have caused harm to others what was the nature of the harm?

6 Do you have a history of alcohol or drug misuse?

These questions are only meant to act as a guide to your own approach.

APPENDIX 2

OUTLINE RISK ASSESSMENT FORMAT

Name . . . .

Date of birth . . . .   ID number. . . . .

Categories of risk identified *(single or multiple – tick relevant boxes)*:

☐ Aggression and violence   ☐ Suicide and self-harm

☐ Severe self-neglect   ☐ Exploitation

☐ Other *(specify)* . . . .

Detail any historical information that may indicate the potential for risk *(for example, personal, family, forensic, social, interpersonal)* . . . .

. . . .

. . . .

. . . .

Detail any health-related factors that may contribute to the potential for risk *(for example, psychiatric symptoms, personality factors, physical disabilities, substance abuse)* . . . .

. . . .

. . . .

. . . .

What risks has the client experienced from others?

. . . .

. . . .

. . . .

Are there any factors that indicate preferred staff allocation *(for example, danger to women, intimidated by men, type of therapeutic approach, need for two workers)*?

. . . .

. . . .

. . . .

What environmental factors may contribute risks *(for example, hostile community, arousal in official/ professional settings, access to drugs, rejection by others, access to weapons)*? . . . .

. . . .

. . . .

. . . .

Are there any organisation/system factors to be considered *(for example, problems of co-ordination, inter-professional/inter-agency differences, waiting lists/delays, reaction to officials)*? . . . .

. . . .

. . . .

. . . .

Is there any current evidence to suggest 'planned intent' to engage in risk-related behaviour?

. . . .

. . . .

. . . .

Is there an immediate need for more detailed risk assessment procedures?

☐ yes ☐ no *(specify reasons)*

. . . .

. . . .

Formulation of assessment for an identified risk:

Category of risk . . . .

If *(name)* . . . .

is in *(situation)* . . . .

. . . .

and/or with *(people)* . . . .

. . . .

then they may begin to *(think)* . . . .

. . . .

and/or *(behave)* . . . .

. . . .

and/or *(experience)* . . . .

. . . .

Early warning signs are . . . .

. . . .

. . . .

and should be discussed with . . . .

In the event of sudden crisis *(consider following actions)* . . . .

. . . .

The probability of this risk is *(high/medium/low)* . . . .

over the following estimated timescale . . . .

based on the available information in the above assessment.

Repeat this formulation for each identified risk on separate sheets of paper.

Interventions will be considered in *Exercise sheet 3.2: Outline risk management plan*.

APPENDIX 3

OUTLINE RISK MANAGEMENT PLAN

Name . . . .

Date of birth . . . .   ID number . . . .

Care Programme Approach registration *(tick all relevant areas)*:

CPA	☐ Yes ☐ No Level......	Supervision Register	☐ Yes	☐ No
Supervised discharge	☐ Yes ☐ No	Section 117	☐ Yes	☐ No
Other section	☐ Yes ☐ No	Care Management	☐ Yes	☐ No

Role of client and/or carer in the plan

Client involved	☐ Yes ☐ No	Carer involved	☐ Yes	☐ No
Client agreed to plan	☐ Yes ☐ No	Carer agreed to plan	☐ Yes	☐ No

Comments . . . .

. . . .

. . . .

Other people involved in the management plan

Psychiatrist	☐ Yes ☐ No	GP	☐ Yes	☐ No
CPN	☐ Yes ☐ No	Occupational therapist	☐ Yes	☐ No
Social worker	☐ Yes ☐ No			

Other(s) *(specify)*

. . . .

Key worker(s) . . . .

. . . .

. . . .

State specifically the identified risk:

X presents a risk of *(categories)* . . . .

. . . .

Through *(behaviours/cognitions)* . . . .

. . . .

In the context of *(situations)*. . . . .

. . . .

Organisational context *(systems)* . . . .

. . . .

Interventions for the above circumstances:

(What). . . . .

(How) . . . .

(When) . . . .

(Who) . . . .

What strengths and opportunities can you identify, from the client and/or the services, as resources to support the management plan? . . . .

. . . .

. . . .

. . . .

What dangers or difficulties may hinder the implementation of the plan? . . . .

. . . .

. . . .

. . . .

. . . .

In the event of breakdown of plan, the following rapid response is required (with responsibilities):

(What) . . . .

(How) . . . .

(When) . . . .

(Who) . . . .

Frequency of review . . . .

Date and place of next review . . . .

Additional comments . . . .

. . . .

. . . .

. . . .

. . . .

. . . .

Key worker signature . . . .

(for collective responsibility)

REFERENCES

Alberg, C., Hatfield, B. and Huxley, P. (Eds.) (1996) *Learning Materials on Mental Health Risk Assessment*. Manchester University Press.

Allen, J., Williamson, S., Gatford, C. & Worthington, A. (1997) Deliberate self-harm: Developing clinical guidelines. *Nursing Standard*, **12** (3) 34–37.

Amos, T. (1998) *Report to Conference on Suicide and Self-harm*. Manchester Conference Centre, 21st January. Brighton: Pavilion Publishing.

Appleby, L. (1992) Suicide in psychiatric patients: Risk and prevention. *British Journal of Psychiatry*, **161**, 749–758.

Appleby, L. (1997) *National Confidential Inquiry into Suicide and Homicide by People with Mental Illness. Progress Report 1997*. London: Department of Health.

Ash, J. (1997) Multidisciplinary audit and the mental health nurse. *Mental Health Care*, **1** (2) 58–60.

Bachrach, L. L. (1988) Defining chronic mental illness: A concept paper. *Hospital and Community Psychiatry*, **39** (4) 383–388.

Bacon, P. (1997) Assessing risk: Are we being overcautious? *British Journal of Psychiatry*, **170** (Supplement 32) 30–31.

Barnes, T. R. E. (1994). The assessment of negative symptoms. In: T. R. E. Barnes and H. E. Nelson (Eds.) *The Assessment of Psychoses: A practical handbook*, pp51–70. London: Chapman & Hall.

Barraclough, B. & Hughes, J. (1987) *Suicide: Clinical and Epidemiological Studies*. Beckenham: Croom Helm.

Bennett, D. (1996) Homicide, inquiries and scapegoating. *Psychiatric Bulletin*, **20**, 298–300.

Bingley, W. (1997) Assessing dangerousness: Protecting the interests of patients. *British Journal of Psychiatry*, **170** (Supplement 32) 28–29.

Borum, R. (1996) Improving the clinical practice of violence risk assessment: Technology, guidelines and training. *American Psychologist*, **51** (9) 945–956.

Bouricius, J. K. (1989) Negative symptoms and emotions in schizophrenia. *Schizophrenia Bulletin*, **15**, 201–207.

References

Bowers H. (1997) *Changing Attitudes to Risk: The Proactive Management of Uncertainty.* Presentation to Anglia and Oxford Region Risk Management Conference, 3rd October, Milton Keynes.

Buchanan, A. (1997) The investigation of acting on delusions as a tool for risk assessment in the mentally disordered. *British Journal of Psychiatry,* **170** (Supplement 32) 12–16.

Burton, P., Low, A. & Briggs, A. (1990) Increasing suicide among young men in England and Wales. *British Medical Journal,* **300**, 1695–1697.

Caldicott, F. (1994) Supervision registers: the College's response. *Psychiatric Bulletin,* **18**, 385–386.

Carson, D. (13 April 1994) *Risk-taking and Risk Assessment in Mental Disorder Services.* Report of study day, Lewisham & Guy's Mental Health NHS Trust, London.

Carson, D. (1995) Calculated Risk. *Community Care,* 26th October–1st November, pp26–27.

Carson, D. (1996) Risking Legal Repercussions. In: H. Kemshall and J. Pritchard (Eds.) *Good Practice in Risk Assessment and Risk Management,* pp3–12. London: Jessica Kingsley.

Chubb, P. (1997) The changing face of risk management: one trust's experience. *The Healthcare Risk Resource,* **1** (1) 2.

Crombie, I. K., Davies, T. O., Abraham, S. C. S. & Florey, C. du V. (1993) *The Audit Handbook: Improving Health Care Through Clinical Audit.* Chichester: Wiley.

Department of Health (1993). *The Health of the Nation, Key Area Handbook: Mental Illness.* London: HMSO.

Department of Health (1995) *Building Bridges: A Guide to Arrangements for Inter-Agency Working for the Care and Protection of Severely Mentally Ill People. The Health of the Nation.* London: HMSO.

Department of Health (1998) *Green Paper: Our Healthier Nation.* London: Department of Health.

Duggan, C. (Ed.) (1997a) Assessing risk in the mentally disordered. *British Journal of Psychiatry,* **170** (Supplement 32) 1–3.

Duggan, M. (1997b) *Pulling Together. The Future Roles and Training of Mental Health Staff.* London: Sainsbury Centre for Mental Health.

Dvoskin, J. A. & Steadman, H. J. (1994) Using intensive case management to reduce violence by mentally ill persons in the community. *Hospital and Community Psychiatry,* **45** (7) 679–684.

Faulk, M.(1994) *Basic Forensic Psychiatry.* Oxford: Blackwell Scientific.

Feaviour, P., Peacock D., Sanderson, H., Bontoft, C. & Wightman, S. (1995) Score Values. *Community Care,* 2–8 November, 28–29.

Fuller Torrey, E. (1994) Violent behaviour by individuals with serious mental illness. *Hospital and Community Psychiatry,* **45** (7) 653–662.

Harris, M. (1997) Training trainers in risk assessment. *British Journal of Psychiatry,* **170** (Supplement 32) 35–36.

Harrison, G. (1997) Risk assessment in a climate of litigation. *British Journal of Psychiatry*, **170** (Supplement 32) 37–39.

Hawton, K. (1994) The Assessment of Suicide Risk. In: T. R. E. Barnes and H. E. Nelson (Eds.) *The Assessment of Psychoses: A practical handbook*, pp125–134. London: Chapman and Hall.

Holloway, F. (1994) Supervision registers: recent government policy and legislation. *Psychiatric Bulletin*, **18**, 593–596.

Home Office and Department of Health (1992) *Review of Health and Social Services for Mentally Disordered Offenders and Others Requiring Similar Services. Final Summary Report (Reed Report).* London: HMSO.

ILPS (1995) *Identification and Management of Risk and Dangerousness: Policy, Staff Procedures and Guidance Notes.* London: Inner London Probation Service.

Jackson, C. & Birchwood, M. (1996) Early Intervention in psychoses: Opportunities for secondary prevention. *British Journal of Clinical Psychology*, **35**, 487–502.

Kreitman, N. (1988) Suicide, age and marital status. *Psychological Medicine*, **18**, 121–128.

Lambeth, Southwark and Lewisham Health Commission (1994) *Local Responses to the Ritchie Report.* Results from three borough-based conferences, held in July and August 1994.

Lipsedge, M. (1995) Clinical risk management in psychiatry. *Quality in Health Care*, **4**, 122–128.

Maden, A. (1996) Risk assessment in psychiatry. *British Journal of Hospital Medicine*, **56** (2/3) 78–82.

Maltsberger, J. T. (1994) Calculated Risks in the Treatment of Intractably Suicidal Patients. *Psychiatry*, **57** (8) 199–211.

Manthorpe, J., Walsh, M., Alasewski, A. & Harrison, L. (1995). Taking a chance. *Community Care*, 19–25 October, 20–21.

McCarthy, A., Roy, D., Holloway, F., Atakan, Z. & Goss, T. (1995) Supervision registers and the care programme approach: a practical solution. *Psychiatric Bulletin*, **19**, 195–199.

McClelland, N. (1995) The assessment of dangerousness: a procedure for predicting potentially dangerous behaviour. *Psychiatric Care*, **2** (1) 17–19.

McDonnell, A., McEvoy, J. & Dearden, R. L. (1994). Coping with violent situations in the caring environment. In: T. Wykes (Ed.) *Violence and Health Care Professionals*, pp189–206. London: Chapman and Hall.

McGovern, J. (1996) Management of risk in psychiatric rehabilitation. *The Psychologist*, September, 405–408.

McGrew, J. H., Bond, G. R., Dietzen, L., McKassen, M. & Miller, M. D. (1995) A multisite study of client outcomes in assertive community treatment. *Psychiatric Services*, **46** (7) 696–701.

Mind (1994) *Report on Deaths Caused by Neuroleptic Drugs.* London: Mind.

Monahan, J. (1993) Limiting therapist exposure to Tarasoff liability: Guidelines for risk containment. *American Psychologist*, **48**, 242–250.

References

Monahan, J. & Arnold, J. (1996) Violence by people with mental illness: A consensus statement by advocates and researchers. *Psychiatric Rehabilitation Journal*, **19** (4) 67–70.

Monahan, J. & Steadman, H. J. (Eds.) (1994) *Violence and Mental Disorder: Developments in Risk Assessment.* Chicago: University of Chicago Press.

Monahan, J. & Steadman, H. J. (1996) Violent storms and violent people. *American Psychologist*, **51** (9) 931–938.

Moore, B. (1996) *Risk Assessment: A Practitioners Guide to Predicting Harmful Behaviour.* London: Whiting and Birch.

Morgan, S. (1996) *Helping Relationships and Mental Health.* Cheltenham: Stanley Thornes.

Morgan, S. (1998) The Assessment and Management of Risk. In: C. Brooker and J. Repper (Eds.) *Serious Mental Illness in the Community.* London: Baillière Tindall.

Muijen, M. (1997a) A man for all reasons. *The Guardian Newspaper*, Society Section, 8th October.

Muijen, M. (1997b). Independent inquiries: why less is more. *Mental Health Practice*, **1** (3) 18–19.

Naughton, J. (1996) The fear of living dangerously. *The Observer Newspaper*, Review Section, 24th March.

Nelson-Jones, R. (1988) *Practical Counselling and Helping Skills*, 2nd ed. London: Cassell.

NHS Executive (1994) *Introduction of Supervision Registers for Mentally Ill People from 1st April 1994.* Health Service Guidelines HSG(94)5. London: NHS Executive.

Ovretveit, J. (1992) *Health Service Quality.* Oxford: Blackwell.

Patterson, B., Leadbetter, D. & Comish, A. (1997). De-escalation in the management of aggression and violence. *Nursing Times*, **93** (36) 58–61.

Phelan, M., Strathdee, G. & Thompson, K. (1997) *Setting Up A Crisis Intervention Service. Mental Health Service Development Skills Workbook.* London: Sainsbury Centre for Mental Health, pp61–64.

Philo, G., Henderson, L. & McLaughlin, G. (1993) *Mass Media Representation of Mental Health/Illness.* Report for the Health Education Board of Scotland. Glasgow: Glasgow University Media Group.

Prins, H. (1986) *Dangerous Behaviour, the Law and Mental Disorder.* London: Tavistock.

Prins, H. (1990) Dangerousness: A review. In: R. Bluglass and P. Bowden (Eds.) *Principles and Practice of Forensic Psychiatry.* Edinburgh: Churchill Livingstone.

Pritchard, C. (1992) Is there a link between suicide in young men and unemployment? A comparison of the UK and other European Community Countries. *British Journal of Psychiatry*, **160**, 750–756.

Reed, J. (1997) Risk assessment and clinical risk management: the lessons from recent inquiries. *British Journal of Psychiatry*, **170** (Supplement 32) 4–7.

Ritchie, J. H., Dick, D. & Lingham. R. (1994) *The Report of the Inquiry into the Care and treatment of Christopher Clunis.* London: HMSO.

Rose, N. (1998) Living dangerously: Risk-thinking and risk management in mental health care. *Mental Health Care*, **1** (8) 263–266.

Roy, D. (1997) Clinical risk management: an merging agenda for psychiatry. *Psychiatric Bulletin*, **21**, 162–164.

Scott, P. D. (1977) Assessing Dangerousness in Criminals. *British Journal of Psychiatry*, **131**, 127–142.

Sheppard, D. (1996) *Learning the Lessons,* 2nd ed. London: The Zito Trust.

Snowden, P. (1997) Practical aspects of clinical risk assessment and management. *British Journal of Psychiatry*, **170** (Supplement 32) 32–34.

Steadman, H. J., Monahan, J., Appelbaum, P. S. *et al.* (1994) Designing a new generation of risk assessment research. In: J. Monahan and H. J. Steadman (Eds.) *Violence and Mental Disorder: Developments in Risk Assessment.* University of Chicago Press.

Turner, M. & Kennedy, M. (1997) Tarasoff and the duty to warn third parties. *Psychiatric Bulletin*, **21** (8) 465–466.

Tyrer, P. & Kennedy, P. (1995) Supervision registers: a necessary component of good psychiatric practice. *Psychiatric Bulletin*, **19**, 193–194.

Vaughan, P. J. (1995) *Suicide Prevention*, 2nd ed. Birmingham: Pepar.

Vaughan, P. J. (1998) The supervision register in practice. *Psychiatric Bulletin*, **22** (6) 1–4.

Vaughan, P. J. & Badger, D. (1995) *Working with the Mentally Disordered Offender in the Community.* Cheltenham: Stanley Thornes.

Vincent, C. (1997) Risk, safety and the dark side of quality. *British Medical Journal*, **314**, 1775–1776.

Warren, J. & Beadsmoore, A. (1997) Preventing violence on mental health wards. *Nursing Times*, **93** (34) 47–48.

Wessely, S. (1997) The epidemiology of crime, violence and schizophrenia. *British Journal of Psychiatry*, **170** (Supplement 32) 8–11.

Whittington, R. & Wykes, T. (1994) The prediction of violence in a health care setting. In: T. Wykes (Ed.) *Violence and Health Care Professionals*, pp. 155–173. London: Chapman and Hall.

Wykes, T, Whittington, R. & Sharrock, R. (1994) The Assessment of Aggression and the Potential for Violence. In: T. R. E. Barnes and H. E. Nelson (Eds.) *The Assessment of Psychoses: A practical handbook.* London: Chapman and Hall.